THE
BEST
ONE STORY HOME PLANS

DESIGNAMERICA

Current Printing (last digit)
10 9 8 7 6 5 4 3 2

1-Story Home Plans
ISBN-13: 978-1-58678-009-8

DESIGN AMERICA, INC.™
www.designamerica.com

The photos on the cover are: Top, Plan #900-101D-0077 on page 52; middle interior photos: Plan #900-101D-0077 on page 52; bottom, left: Plan #900-032D-0826 on page 56; .bottom, right: Plan #900-032D-0930 on page 21.

Contents

Top to bottom: Plan #900-101D-0089 on page 25; Plan #900-011D-0007 on page 57; Plan #900-101D-0056, on page 81; Plan #900-011D-0342 on page 61; Plan #900-076D-0280 on page 33; Plan #900-051D-0981 on page 22.

why buy stock plans?

Building a home presents an opportunity to showcase your creativity and turn dreams into reality. With this opportunity, challenges and questions crop up. Location, size, and budget are all important, as well as features and amenities. When you begin, it may seem overwhelming. But before you get anxious, search for a stock home and make the process easier.

Both custom and stock home plans have positives and negatives; what is "best" can be determined by your lifestyle, budget, and time-frame. A custom home plan is one that a homeowner and architect develop together by putting ideas down on paper. It requires extra time and added patience.

A stock plan is a pre-developed plan that fits the needs of many in the general population. They are available within days of purchasing and cost considerably less than custom plans, yet they have the amenities you want at a more affordable price.

Some homeowners fear a stock home will simply be a copy, which takes away from owning a home that's truly unique. This is a common misconception that wastes money and time!

The variety of stock plans available is very impressive. Browse the plans in this book, and find a plan perfect for your needs. And remember, stock plans are customizable. Maybe you found a plan that's almost perfect, but you need a larger mud room. Our customizing service can modify the stock plan and create a version just for you. Stock plans often have a material list available too, which helps eliminate unknown costs during construction.

Thanks to stock plans you will be on your way to building your dream home in no time and for much less money!

what's the right plan for you?

Choosing a house design is exciting, but can be a difficult task. Many factors play a role in what home plan is best for you and your family. To help you get started, we have pinpointed some of the major factors to consider when searching for your dream home. Take the time to evaluate your family's needs and you will have an easier time sorting through all of the house designs offered in this book.

BUDGET is the first thing to consider. Many items take part in this budget, from ordering the blueprints to the last doorknob purchased. When you find the perfect house plan, visit houseplansandmore.com and get a cost-to-build estimate to ensure that the finished home will be within your cost range. A cost-to-build report is a detailed summary that gives you the total cost to build a specific home in the zip code where you're wanting to build. It is interactive allowing you to adjust labor and material costs, and it's created on demand when ordered so all pricing is up-to-date. This valuable tool will help you know how much your dream home will cost before you buy plans (see page 96 for more information).

MAKE A LIST

Experts in the field suggest that the best way to determine your needs is to begin by listing everything you like or dislike about your current home.

FAMILY LIFESTYLE After your budget is deciphered, you need to assess you and your family's lifestyle needs. Think about the stage of life you are in now, and what stages you will be going through in the future. Ask yourself questions to figure out how much room you need now and if you will need room for expansion. Are you married? Do you have children? How many children do you plan on having? Are you an empty-nester? How long do you plan to live in this home?

Incorporate into your planning any frequent guests you may have, including elderly parents, grandchildren or adult children who may live with you.

Does your family entertain a lot? If so, think about the rooms you will need to do so. Will you need both formal and informal spaces? Do you need a gourmet kitchen? Do you need a game room and/or a wet bar?

FLOOR PLAN LAYOUTS When looking through these home plans, imagine yourself walking through the house. Consider the flow from the entry to the living, sleeping and gathering areas. Does the layout ensure privacy for the master bedroom? Does the garage enter near the kitchen for easy unloading? Does the placement of the windows provide enough privacy from any neighboring properties? Do you plan on using furniture you already have? Will this furniture fit in the appropriate rooms? When you find a plan you want to purchase, be sure to picture yourself actually living in it.

EXTERIOR SPACES With many different styles of one-story homes throughout this book, flip through these pages and find which one-story style appeals to you the most and think about the neighborhood in which you plan to build. Also, think about how the house will fit on your site. Picture the landscaping you want to add to the lot. Using your imagination is key when choosing a home plan.

Choosing a house design can be an intimidating experience. Asking yourself these questions before you get started on the search will help you through the process. With our large selection of sizes and styles, we are certain you will find your dream home in this book.

10 steps to BUILDING your dream home

1 TALK TO A LENDER

If you plan to obtain a loan in order to build your new home, then it's best to find out first how much you can get approved for before selecting a home design. Knowing the financial information before you start looking for land or a home will keep you from selecting something out of your budget and turning a great experience into a major disappointment. Financing the home you plan to build is somewhat different than financing the purchase of an existing house. You're going to need thousands of dollars for land, labor, and materials. Chances are, you're going to have to borrow most of it. Therefore, you will probably need to obtain a construction loan. This is a short-term loan to pay for building your house. When the house is completed, the loan is paid off in full, usually out of the proceeds from your long-term mortgage loan.

2 DETERMINE NEEDS

Selecting the right home plan for your needs and lifestyle requires a lot of thought. Your new home is an investment, so you should consider not only your current needs, but also your future requirements. Versatility and the potential for converting certain areas to other uses could be an important factor later on. So, although a home office may seem unnecessary now, in years to come, the idea may seem ideal. Home plans that include flex spaces or bonus rooms can really adapt to your needs in the future.

3 CHOOSE A HOMESITE

The site for your new home will have a definite impact on the design you select. It's a good idea to select a home that will complement your site. This will save you time and money when building. Or, you can then modify a design to specifically accommodate your site. However, it will most likely make your home construction more costly than selecting a home plan suited for your lot right from the start. For example, if your land slopes, a walk-out basement works perfectly. If it's wooded, or has a lake in the back, an atrium ranch home is a perfect style to take advantage of surrounding backyard views.

SOME IMPORTANT CRITERIA TO CONSIDER WHEN CHOOSING A HOMESITE:

- Improvements will have to be made including utilities, walks and driveways
- Convenience of the lot to work, school, shops, etc.
- Zoning requirements and property tax amounts
- Soil conditions at your future site
- Make sure the person or firm that sells you the land owns it free and clear

4 SELECT A HOME DESIGN

We've chosen the "best of the best" of the one-story home plans found at houseplansandmore.com to be featured in this book. With over 19,000 home plans from the best architects and designers across North America, this book includes the best variety of styles and sizes to suit the needs and tastes of a broad spectrum of homeowners.

5 GET THE COST TO BUILD

If you feel you have found "the" home, then before taking the step of purchasing house plans, order an estimated cost-to-build report for the exact zip code where you plan to build. Requesting this custom

cost report created specifically for you will help educate you on all costs associated with building your new home. Simply order this report and gain knowledge of the material and labor cost associated with the home you love. Not only does the report allow you to choose the quality of the materials, you can also select options in every aspect of the project from lot condition to contractor fees. This report will allow you to successfully manage your construction budget in all areas, clearly see where the majority of the costs lie, and save you money from start to finish.

A COST TO BUILD REPORT WILL DETERMINE THE OVERALL COST OF YOU RNEW HOME INCLUSING THESE 5 MAJOR EXPENSE CATEGORIES:

- Land
- Foundation
- Materials
- General Contractor's fee - Some rules-of-thumb that you may find useful are: (a) the total labor cost will generally run a little higher than your total material cost, but it's not unusual for a builder or general contractor to charge 15-20% of the combined cost for managing the overall project.
- Site improvements - don't forget to add in the cost of your site improvements such as utilities, driveway, sidewalks, landscaping, etc.

6 HIRE A CONTRACTOR

If you're inexperienced in construction, you'll probably want to hire a general contractor to manage the project. If you do not know a reputable general contractor, begin your search by contacting your local Home Builders Association to get references. Many states require building contractors to be licensed. If this is the case in your state, its licensing board is another referral source. Finding a reputable, quality-minded contractor is a key factor in ensuring that your new home is well constructed and is finished on time and within budget. It can be a smart decision to discuss the plan you like with your builder prior to ordering plans. They can guide you into choosing the right type of plan package option especially if you intend on doing some customizing to the design.

7 CUSTOMIZING

Sometimes your general contractor may want to be the one who makes the modifications you want to the home you've selected. But, sometimes they want to receive the plans ready to build. That is why we offer home plan modification services. Please see page 99 for specific information on the customizing process and how to get a free quote on the changes you want to make to a home before you buy the plans.

8 ORDER HOME PLANS

If you've found the home and are ready to order blueprints, we recommend ordering the PDF file format, which offers the most flexibility. A PDF file format will be emailed to you when you order, and it includes a copyright release from the designer, meaning you have the legal right to make changes to the plan if necessary as well as print out as many copies of the plan as you need for building the home one-time. You will be happy to have your blueprints saved electronically so they can easily be shared with your contractor, subcontractors, lender and local building officials. We do, however, offer several different types of plan package depending on your needs, so please refer to page 97 for all plan options available and choose the best one for your particular situation.

Another helpful component in the building process that is available for many of the house plans in this book is a material list. A material list includes not only a detailed list of materials, but it also indicates where various cuts of lumber and other building components are to be used. This will save your general contractor significant time and money since they won't have to create this list before building begins. If a material list is available for a home, it is indicated in the plan data box on the specific plan page in this book.

9 ORDER MATERIALS

You can order materials yourself, or have your contractor do it. Nevertheless, in order to thoroughly enjoy your new home you will want to personally select many of the materials that go into its construction. Today, home improvement stores offer a wide variety of quality building products. Only you can decide what specific types of windows, cabinets, bath fixtures, etc. will make your new home yours. Spend time early on in the construction process looking at the materials and products available.

10 MOVE IN

With careful planning and organization, your new home will be built on schedule and ready for your move-in date. Be sure to have all of your important documents in place for the closing of your new home and then you'll be ready to move in and start living your dream.

Look no further than One-Story Home Plans to discover the best single level home plans available today. We've taken the "best of the best" from all of the top designers and architects across North America and brought them to you in one publication. No more searching through thousands of home designs on-line, these are the top 100 one-story home designs offered in a huge variety of sizes and styles to suit many tastes. From Craftsman and Country, to Modern and Traditional, there is a One-story home plan here for everyone, and with all of the amenities and features homeowners are looking for when building a new home today. Start your search for the perfect One-story home right now!

Top, left: Plan #900-011S-0101 on page 18; top, right: Plan #900-007D-0010 on page 14; bottom, left: Plan #900-065D-0426 on page 28; bottom, right: Plan #900-101D-0045, on page 55.

why a ONE-STORY home?

Countless homes continue to be designed to suit everyone's needs and desires. However, it is undeniable that many homeowners building a new home are looking for a long-term solution and place to settle. No one puts the time and effort into building a new home they will only occupy for a mere moment. Keeping this in mind, it's important to look around and recognize that building a one-story home is a popular trend in new home construction.

Two-story homes have quite a bit to offer busy families and those on a budget. They allow you to use the property to its fullest by building up and creating more living space without purchasing additional land. However, as the baby boomer generation continues to grow older and their spending power allows them to continue to build homes, space is not the first priority on aging minds. Indeed, what good is great space if it becomes too difficult to access? Many baby boomers are looking to the future, building dream homes in which they can live out the rest of their lives. Homes that are open, universally designed to handle physical limitations and still luxurious for entertaining family and friends. Retirees still want enough space they can access independently. The one-story home is a dream home capable of fulfilling this desire. Multi-generational families composed of all ages can also appreciate the ease of one-story living thanks to their typically open floor plan and airy atmosphere making it feel larger than its true size.

One-story homes do not require regular taxing use of steps and stairways, granting access to the entire home for those with limited mobility. Additionally, thoughtful and open layouts make households easier to maintain. For example, bedrooms are typically located closely to the laundry area or mud room greatly minimizing the work of transporting laundry loads up and down the stairs. The kitchen is also located near the bedrooms and other general spaces with immediate access to the garage, too.

It is important to note that one-story homes don't lack variety and architectural interest. One recommendation for outfitting a single story home is to create dynamic views. Varying window and ceiling heights and styles can be combined to create dramatic vistas from any point in a room. Spacious family rooms can boast grand ceilings and wall-sized picture windows, both of which are extremely popular in today's home designs. Not only can you expand the interior spaces of a one-story home out, but also up with soaring ceilings.

Top, left: Plan #900-011S-0018 on page 59; bottom, right: Plan #900-011D-0347 on page 37.

Here are a few reasons why homeowners are drawn to one-level living. With ease of movement, expansive room sizes, and convenience to and from every space in the house, this type of floor plan is more popular than ever.

sloping lot, not a downfall

Sloping lots are anything but a downfall. Building a new home even if you don't have a flat plot of land is possible. Sloping lots offer the ideal location to build an atrium ranch home, for example. With sweeping windows along the entire rear wall, the house will be flooded with natural light. The added light adds dimension to the interior, while creating an impressive looking exterior. Or, how about building a ranch with a finished walk-out basement? If you have a sloping lot, select an atrium ranch, or a home with a lower level that offers the possibility of expanding.

maximize space

Combined spaces equal twice the function. One-story homes can offer more flexibility than multi-level homes. Living spaces without another level overhead permit vaulted ceilings, dramatic windows and the use of skylights or transoms to add spaciousness. Many ranch homes offer open floor plans created by combining the great room, dining space and kitchen to form the main gathering place. These areas when topped with a vaulted ceiling provide an impressive and highly functional space. Less walls means more square footage being maximized.

easy entertaining

With many one-story homes having the ability to finish a lower level, an open lower level with state-of-the-art amenities is perfect for families that love to entertain and have frequent guests. While, the homeowners are still able to maintain a sense of privacy on the main level. A lower level is ideal for having fun with family and friends, or enjoying your favorite hobbies.

expand

Move one-story living to the outdoors with an amazing outdoor living space that is now a mainstay in new homebuilding. Many one-stories include fantastic outdoor living spaces, great for entertaining, everyday living, or enjoying a hobby like gardening. An outdoor kitchen is a fantastic amenity that keeps the cook and guests in close proximity to one another. And, an ever-popular outdoor fireplace warms an outdoor area so it can be enjoyed all year long. These spaces expand living beyond a home's walls and many offer a very seamless transition between the indoor and outdoor spaces.

special details

Amenities are found throughout every home no matter how many floors it has, but decorative ceilings and unique lighting can really enhance a one-story home quite easily and effectively. Seamless decorating from room to room creates a more open feel as well.

One-story homes are increasingly popular because they make a perfect starter home for new homeowners, while also having an ideal layout for those downsizing, or retiring. While a choice of homes is largely based on personal preference, one-story homes should be kept in mind when determining what home to build. One-story abodes have quite a bit to offer, just as every dream home should.

Plan #900-051D-0960

Dimensions: 117' W x 50'8" D
Heated Sq. Ft.: 2,784
Bedrooms: 3   Bathrooms: 2
Exterior Walls: 2" x 6"
Foundation: Basement standard; crawl space or slab for an additional fee
See index on page 95 for more information

Features

- You are welcomed into the home with 11' ceilings that top the great room and kitchen
- All three bedrooms, including the master bedroom, are located to the right when entering the home
- The master bedroom includes a bath with a Jacuzzi tub, dual sinks, as well as a spacious walk-in closet
- The other two bedrooms share a full bath nearby
- There is a large screened-in porch behind the garage
- 3-car front entry garage

Images provided by designer/architect

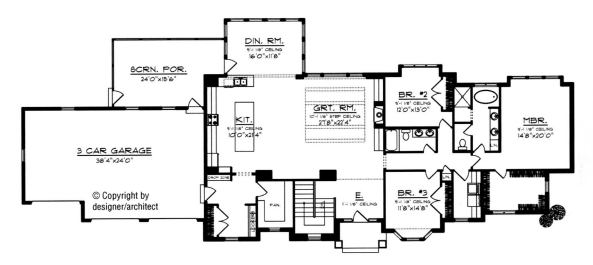

DIN. RM.
9'-1 1/8" CEILING
16'0"x11'8"

SCRN. POR.
24'0"x15'6"

GRT. RM.
10'-1 1/8" STEP CEILING
27'8"x22'4"

KIT.
9'-1 1/8" CEILING
10'0"x21'4"

BR. #2
9'-1 1/8" CEILING
12'0"x13'0"

MBR.
9'-1 1/8" CEILING
14'8"x20'0"

3 CAR GARAGE
38'4"x24'0"

© Copyright by designer/architect

E.
11'-1 1/8" CEILING

BR. #3
9'-1 1/8" CEILING
11'8"x14'8"

Plan #900-076D-0220

Dimensions:	97'2" W x 87'7" D
Heated Sq. Ft.:	3,061
Bonus Sq. Ft.:	3,644
Bedrooms: 3	Bathrooms: 3½

Foundation: Basement, crawl space or slab, please specify when ordering
See index on page 95 for more information

Images provided by designer/architect

© Copyright by designer/architect

Features

- The first floor is open and airy with the main gathering spaces combining perfectly for maximizing the square footage
- The kitchen is open to the family room with a grilling terrace nearby
- The optional lower level has an additional 2,975 square feet of living area including two bedrooms, a full bath, a hobby room, a theater, an office, and a recreation area with a bar
- The optional second floor has an additional 669 square feet of living area with 277 square feet in the bedroom and 392 square feet in the recreation area
- 3-car front entry garage

First Floor
3,061 sq. ft.

Optional
Lower Level
2,975 sq. ft.

Optional
Second Floor
669 sq. ft.

Images provided by designer/architect

Plan #900-163D-0003

Dimensions:	56' W x 40' D
Heated Sq. Ft.:	1,416
Bedrooms: 3	Bathrooms: 2
Exterior Walls:	2" x 6"
Foundation:	Crawl space

See index on page 95 for more information

Features

- The great room is open to both the kitchen and dining area on the left side of the house for an open, airy feel
- All three bedrooms are located on the right side of the house with the master suite having a private sitting porch
- The laundry room is conveniently located just off of the kitchen

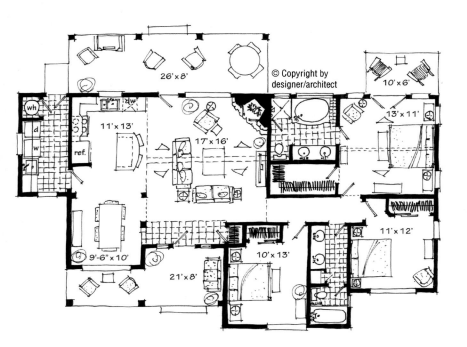

Plan #900-007D-0010

Dimensions:	83' W x 42'4" D
Heated Sq. Ft.:	1,845
Bonus Sq. Ft.:	889
Bedrooms: 3	Bathrooms: 2

Foundation: Walk-out basement standard; crawl space or slab for an additional fee

See index on page 95 for more information

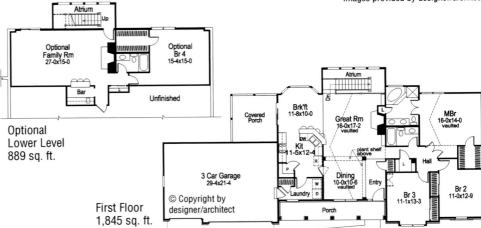

Optional Lower Level 889 sq. ft.

First Floor 1,845 sq. ft.

© Copyright by designer/architect

Plan #900-028D-0099

Dimensions:	30' W x 49' D
Heated Sq. Ft.:	1,320
Bedrooms: 3	Bathrooms: 2
Exterior Walls:	2" x 6"
Foundation:	Monolithic slab

See index on page 95 for more information

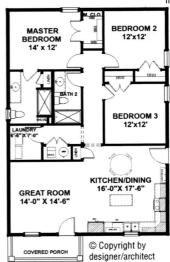

© Copyright by designer/architect

call toll-free 1-800-373-2646   houseplansandmore.com

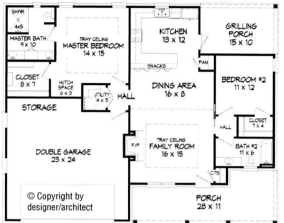

Plan #900-141D-0143

Dimensions: 52'7" W x 43'8" D
Heated Sq. Ft.: 1,340
Bedrooms: 2   Bathrooms: 2
Foundation: Slab standard; crawl space, basement or walk-out basement for an additional fee

See index on page 95 for more information

Plan #900-016D-0049

Dimensions: 69'10" W x 51'8" D
Heated Sq. Ft.: 1,793
Bonus Sq. Ft.: 779
Bedrooms: 3   Bathrooms: 2
Foundation: Slab or crawl space standard; basement for an additional fee

See index on page 95 for more information

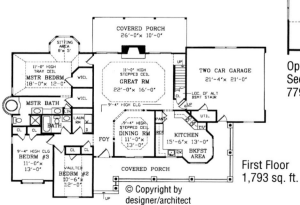

Optional
Second Floor
779 sq. ft.

First Floor
1,793 sq. ft.

Plan #900-155D-0027

Dimensions:	72'2" W x 71'6" D
Heated Sq. Ft.:	2,513
Bedrooms: 5	Bathrooms: 3½

Foundation: Crawl space or slab,
please specify when ordering
See index on page 95 for more information

Images provided by designer/architect

Features

- Timber posts and exposed truss beams create a Craftsman inspired interior
- This stylish home has a great layout for family living
- The kitchen is centrally located and is steps from the vaulted great room with a cozy fireplace
- The master suite enjoys double walk-in closets, and a private bath
- The outdoor covered porch has a vaulted ceiling, and a handsome fireplace for extending time outdoors further into the Fall
- 2-car side entry garage

Plan #900-011D-0229

Dimensions:	60' W x 111' D
Heated Sq. Ft.:	2,904
Bedrooms: 3	Bathrooms: 3½
Exterior Walls:	2" x 6"

Foundation: Joisted crawl space, post & beam, or TrusJoist floor system standard; slab or basement for an additional fee

See index on page 95 for more information

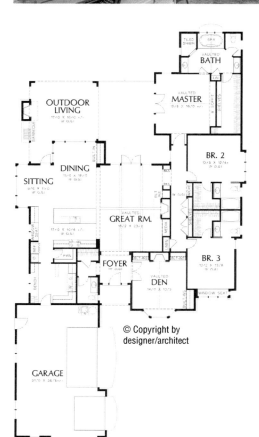

Features

- This stunning one-story has all of the essentials for great family living
- The kitchen features an island facing out over the dining area with a nearby sitting and great room
- The bedrooms are all in close proximity to one another for convenience
- A cozy vaulted den has a fireplace and a bay window
- The outdoor living space has a fireplace and built-in grill
- 3-car side entry garage

© Copyright by designer/architect

Images provided by designer/architect

Plan #900-011S-0101

Dimensions: 96' W x 65' D
Heated Sq. Ft.: 3,296
Bedrooms: 3   Bathrooms: 3½
Exterior Walls: 2" x 6"
Foundation: Joisted crawl space or
post & beam standard; slab or
basement for an additional fee
See index on page 95 for more information

Images provided by designer/architect

Features

- Craftsman, Prairie and Modern styles merge to form a home with a rustic exterior and clean, modern lines
- The vaulted great room is expansive and seamlessly flows into the kitchen for a wonderful gathering spot that's ready for the challenges of everyday family life, or entertaining
- The kitchen is centralized between both casual and more formal dining options
- The master bedroom has sliding glass doors, a free-standing built-in dresser that acts as a partition between the bath and bedroom, and a cozy fireplace
- The office is designed for great functionality with a built-in desk and bookcase
- 3-car front entry garage

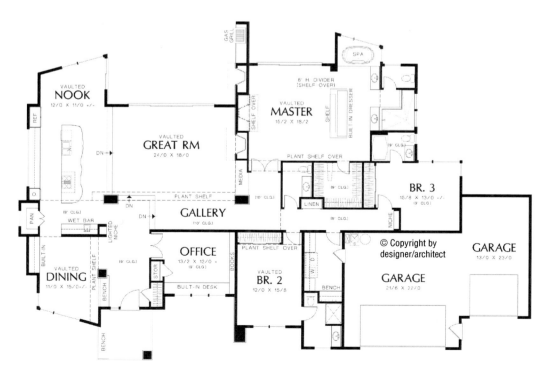

Floor plan labels:

VAULTED
NOOK
12/0 X 11/0 +/-

VAULTED
GREAT RM
24/0 X 18/0

VAULTED
MASTER
15/2 X 18/2

8' H. DIVIDER
(SHELF OVER)

SPA

GAS GRILL

REF

SHELF OVER

BUILT-IN DRESSER

PLANT SHELF OVER

MEDIA

BR. 3
15/8 X 13/0 +/-
(9' CLG.)

LINEN

PLANT SHELF

GALLERY
(10' CLG.)

NICHE

PAN

WET BAR

LIGHTED NICHE

DN

OFFICE
13/2 X 12/0 +
(9' CLG.)

BOOKS

PLANT SHELF OVER

© Copyright by
designer/architect

GARAGE
13/0 X 23/0

BUILT-IN

VAULTED
DINING
11/0 X 15/0 +/-

PLANT SHELF

BENCH

STOR.

BUILT-IN DESK

VAULTED
BR. 2
12/0 X 15/8

W./D.

BENCH

GARAGE
21/6 X 22/0

BENCH

Plan #900-091D-0510

Dimensions: 76' W x 60'2" D
Heated Sq. Ft.: 2,125
Bonus Sq. Ft.: 427
Bedrooms: 3   Bathrooms: 2½
Exterior Walls: 2" x 6"
Foundation: Basement or crawl space standard; slab or walk-out basement for an additional fee

See index on page 95 for more information

Optional
Second Floor
427 sq. ft.

First Floor
2,125 sq. ft.

Plan #900-007D-0060

Dimensions: 38'8" W x 48'4" D
Heated Sq. Ft.: 1,268
Bedrooms: 3   Bathrooms: 2
Foundation: Basement standard; crawl space or slab for an additional fee

See index on page 95 for more information

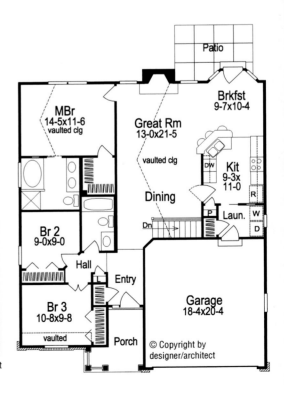

call toll-free 1-800-373-2646   houseplansandmore.com

Plan #900-077D-0259

Images provided by designer/architect

Dimensions: 55' W x 48' D
Heated Sq. Ft.: 1,870
Bedrooms: 3 **Bathrooms: 2½**
Foundation: Slab or crawl space, please specify when ordering
See index on page 95 for more information

Covered Porch
30-10 x 8-0

Bedroom 2
12-6 x 11-0
9' Clg. Ht.

Kitchen
9-0 x 14-6

Laundry
10x7

Flex Space
11-0 x 11-0
9' Clg. Ht.

Eating Area
10-8 x 14-6
9' Clg. Ht.

Island

Ref.
Pan.

Hall 1

Half Bath
7'-8"x5

Master Closet
9-6 x 6-8

Lin.

Hall 2

Bath 2

Great Room
19-8 x 18-6
10' Clg. Ht.
(All sizes are clear)

Gas Log

Master Bedroom
11-8 x 14-6
10' Clg. Ht.
Trayed Clg.

Master Bath
9-6 x 15

Lin.

Jet Tub

Bedroom 3
12-6 x 11-6
9' Clg. Ht.

Shwr

Covered Porch
31-0 x 6-0

© Copyright by designer/architect

Images provided by designer/architect

Plan #900-032D-0930

Dimensions: 54'8" W x 48' D
Heated Sq. Ft.: 1,676
Bedrooms: 2 **Bathrooms: 1**
Exterior Walls: 2" x 6"
Foundation: Basement standard; crawl space, floating slab or monolithic slab for an additional fee
See index on page 95 for more information

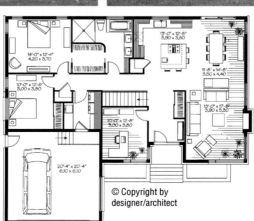

14'-0" x 12'-4"
4,20 x 3,70

13'-0" x 12'-8"
3,90 x 3,80

10'-0" x 12'-8"
3,00 x 3,80

11'-8" x 14'-8"
3,50 x 4,40

13'-0" x 17'-6"
3,90 x 5,30

10'-0" x 12'-8"
3,00 x 3,80

20'-4" x 20'-4"
6,10 x 6,10

© Copyright by designer/architect

Plan #900-051D-0981

Images provided by designer/architect

Dimensions: 55'4" W x 71'8" D
Heated Sq. Ft.: 2,005
Bedrooms: 3   Bathrooms: 2
Exterior Walls: 2" x 6"
Foundation: Basement standard; crawl space or slab for an additional fee
See index on page 95 for more information

Features

- The master suite is located just off the great room and boasts dual sinks and a generously sized walk-in closet in its private bath
- There is easy access to the laundry room from the master closet which makes tackling dirty laundry a breeze
- The kitchen island looks out into the open great room and dining area giving a very open feeling
- The second and third bedrooms are situated in the front left of the house, with the master bedroom in the back right for privacy
- You can walk out onto the covered porch from the dining room for a view of the backyard
- 3-car front entry garage

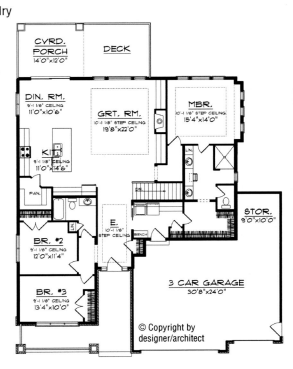

© Copyright by designer/architect

Plan #900-013D-0230

Dimensions:	53'8" W x 60'1" D
Heated Sq. Ft.:	1,800
Bonus Sq. Ft.:	3,124
Bedrooms: 3	Bathrooms: 2½

Foundation: Walk-out basement standard; crawl space or slab for an additional fee

See index on page 95 for more information

Images provided by designer/architect

Features

- The beautiful master suite boasts a sitting area, corner bathtub and expansive his and hers closet
- The optional lower level has an additional 1,900 square feet of living area and provides a perfect area for hosting guests with a guest suite including a kitchen, living area, theater, recreation area and even a terrace
- The optional second floor has an additional 1,224 square feet of living area
- 2-car side entry garage

© Copyright by designer/architect

Optional Lower Level 1,900 sq. ft.

First Floor 1,800 sq. ft.

Optional Second Floor 1,224 sq. ft.

Plan #900-161D-0013

Dimensions:	99'4" W x 87'10" D
Heated Sq. Ft.:	3,264
Bedrooms: 3	Bathrooms: 3½
Exterior Walls:	2" x 6"
Foundation:	Crawl space

See index on page 95 for more information

Images provided by designer/architect

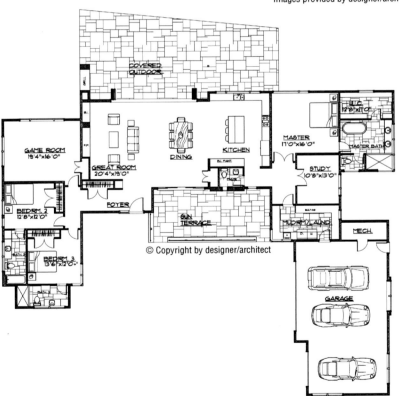

© Copyright by designer/architect

Features

- This stunning modern home offers the open floor plan and high ceilings homeowners want today
- The split bedroom floor plan has the master suite tucked behind the kitchen and near a quiet study
- There are lovely outdoor spaces in the front as well as the back of the home
- The great room enjoys a sleek fireplace that can also be seen by the kitchen and dining space
- 3-car side entry garage

Plan #900-101D-0089

Dimensions:	70' W x 77'9" D
Heated Sq. Ft.:	2,509
Bonus Sq. Ft.:	1,645
Bedrooms: 4	Bathrooms: 2½
Exterior Walls:	2" x 6"
Foundation:	Basement

See index on page 95 for more information

Images provided by designer/architect

Features

- The wrap around porch welcomes you into this beautiful airy home designed with a popular Modern Farmhouse flair
- Expansive windows bring so much natural light into every room
- The desirable split bedroom layout of this home is perfect for families
- The dining, kitchen and great room are all open, creating one large open family area, perfect for all activities from dining to relaxing
- With a walk-in closet, dual sinks and a generously sized bedroom, the master suite makes for a perfect place to retire for the evening
- The optional lower level has an additional 1,645 square feet of living area and includes two additional bedrooms and a bath plus a rec room with a wet bar
- 3-car side entry garage

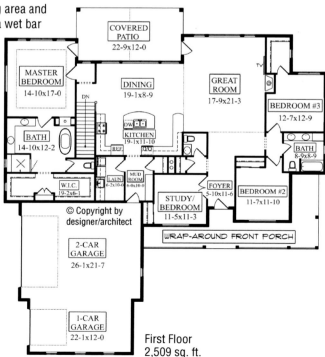

First Floor
2,509 sq. ft.

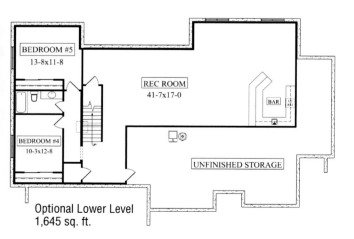

Optional Lower Level
1,645 sq. ft.

Plan #900-011D-0637

Dimensions: 46'6" W x 54' D
Heated Sq. Ft.: 1,744
Bedrooms: 3   Bathrooms: 2½
Exterior Walls: 2" x 6"
Foundation: Engineered joists with crawl space standard; slab or basement for an additional fee

See index on page 95 for more information

© Copyright by designer/architect

Plan #900-159D-0007

Dimensions: 64' W x 59' D
Heated Sq. Ft.: 1,850
Bonus Sq. Ft.: 1,300
Bedrooms: 3   Bathrooms: 2½
Exterior Walls: 2" x 6"
Foundation: Basement or walk-out basement, please specify when ordering

See index on page 95 for more information

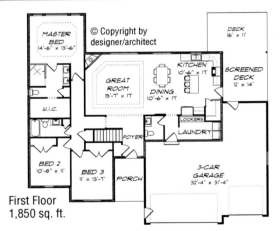

© Copyright by designer/architect

First Floor
1,850 sq. ft.

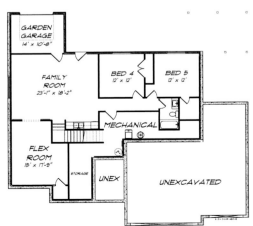

Optional
Lower Level
1,300 sq. ft.

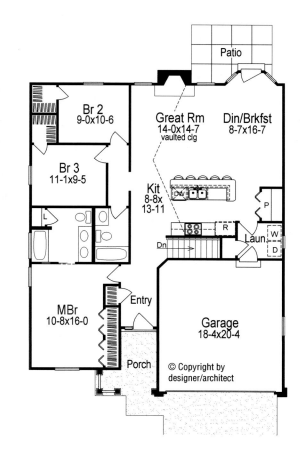

Plan #900-007D-5060

Images provided by designer/architect

Dimensions: 36' W x 46'4" D
Heated Sq. Ft.: 1,344
Bedrooms: 3 Bathrooms: 2
Foundation: Basement standard; crawl space or slab for an additional fee
See index on page 95 for more information

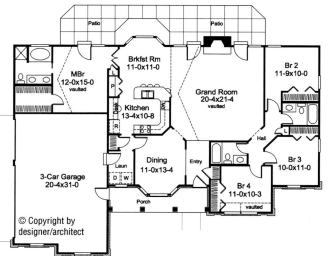

Plan #900-007D-0146

Images provided by designer/architect

Dimensions: 68' W x 49'8" D
Heated Sq. Ft.: 1,929
Bedrooms: 4 Bathrooms: 3
Foundation: Crawl space standard; slab or basement for an additional fee
See index on page 95 for more information

Images provided by designer/architect

Plan #900-065D-0426

Dimensions: 54'5" W x 57'3" D
Heated Sq. Ft.: 1,718
Bedrooms: 3   Bathrooms: 2
Foundation: Basement standard; crawl space, slab, or walk-out basement for an additional fee
See index on page 95 for more information

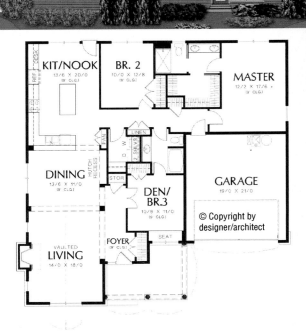

Images provided by designer/architect

Plan #900-011D-0224

Dimensions: 50' W x 52' D
Heated Sq. Ft.: 1,802
Bedrooms: 3   Bathrooms: 2
Exterior Walls: 2" x 6"
Foundation: Joisted crawl space or post & beam standard; slab or basement for an additional fee
See index on page 95 for more information

Plan #900-056D-0122

Dimensions: 63'9" W x 63'6" D
Heated Sq. Ft.: 1,338
Bedrooms: 3   Bathrooms: 2
Foundation: Slab standard; crawl space
for an additional fee
See index on page 95 for more information

Images provided by designer/architect

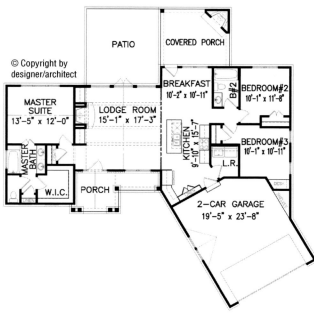

Plan #900-051D-0972

Dimensions: 38' W x 74' D
Heated Sq. Ft.: 1,490
Bedrooms: 2   Bathrooms: 2
Exterior Walls: 2" x 6"
Foundation: Basement standard; crawl
space or slab for an additional fee
See index on page 95 for more information

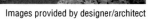

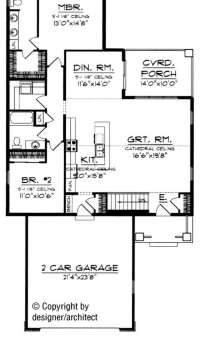

Images provided by designer/architect

Plan #900-101D-0094

Dimensions:	72' W x 72'9" D
Heated Sq. Ft.:	2,650
Bonus Sq. Ft.:	1,821
Bedrooms: 3	Bathrooms: 2½
Exterior Walls:	2" x 6"
Foundation:	Basement

See index on page 95 for more information

Images provided by designer/architect

Features

- Sleek Prairie-inspired exterior is refreshing and uncomplicated creating great curb appeal
- The open first floor has a private master suite, two bedrooms, and a study
- The optional lower level has an additional 1,821 square feet of living area and includes a large recreation room with a wet bar, two additional bedrooms and a full bath, plus a wine room
- 3-car front entry garage

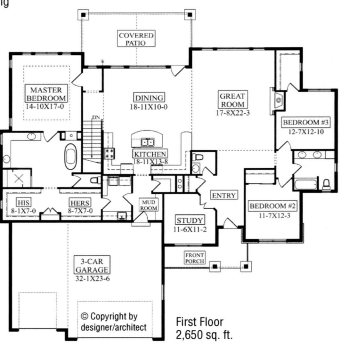

First Floor
2,650 sq. ft.

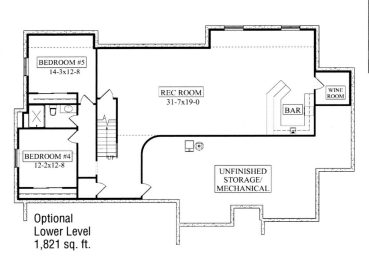

Optional
Lower Level
1,821 sq. ft.

Images provided by designer/architect

Plan #900-155D-0029

Dimensions: 90'6" W x 73'6" D
Heated Sq. Ft.: 3,385
Bonus Sq. Ft.: 638
Bedrooms: 4   Bathrooms: 3½
Foundation: Crawl space or slab
standard; basement or daylight
basement for an additional fee
See index on page 95 for more information

Features

- The massive kitchen island has enough seating for six people, and doesn't miss the action in the great room
- An outdoor living/grilling porch has a vaulted ceiling and a cozy outdoor fireplace for those chilly nights
- Both informal and formal dining options are available in this floor plan
- The optional second floor bonus room has an additional 638 square feet of living area
- 2-car side entry garage, and a 1-car front entry garage

Optional
Second Floor
638 sq. ft.

© Copyright by
designer/architect

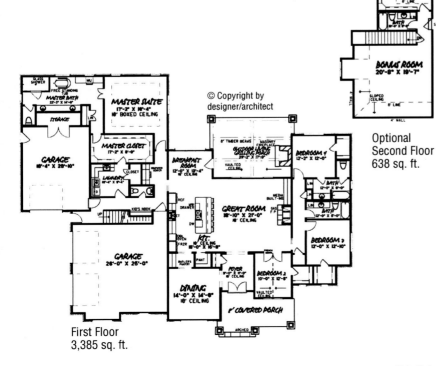

First Floor
3,385 sq. ft.

Plan #900-056S-0019

Dimensions:	121'5" W x 107'9" D
Heated Sq. Ft.:	3,480
Bonus Sq. Ft.:	1,031
Bedrooms: 3	Bathrooms: 3½

Foundation: Basement standard; crawl space or slab for an additional fee

See index on page 95 for more information

Images provided by designer/architect

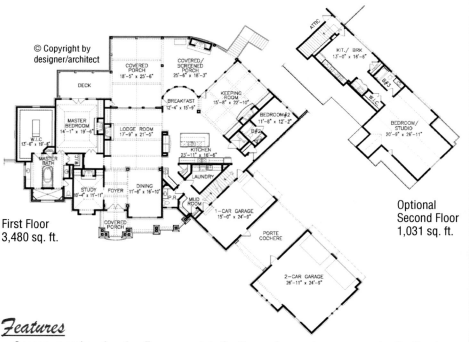

© Copyright by designer/architect

First Floor
3,480 sq. ft.

Optional
Second Floor
1,031 sq. ft.

Features

- Gorgeous and enchanting European style Craftsman home shows so much attention to detail inside and out
- The first floor features so many extra amenities such as a study, a keeping room with a fireplace, a covered screened porch with a fireplace, and a formal dining room
- There are also fireplaces in the master bedroom and the lodge room for a cozy feel at every turn
- Both a mud room and laundry room keep this home high functioning
- The optional second floor has an additional 1,031 square feet of living area and includes a studio apartment with a kitchen/breakfast area, a full bath and a bedroom. 2-car rear entry
- 2-car rear entry garage, and a 1-car rear entry garage

Plan #900-005D-0001

Dimensions: 72' W x 34'4" D
Heated Sq. Ft.: 1,400
Bedrooms: 3   Bathrooms: 2
Foundation: Basement standard; crawl space or slab for an additional fee
See index on page 95 for more information

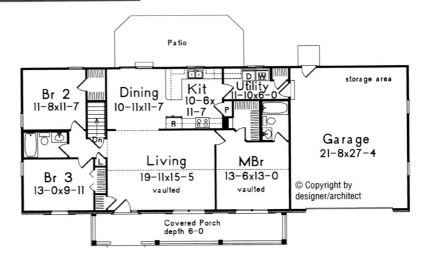

Plan #900-157D-0023

Dimensions: 65'11" W x 107' D
Heated Sq. Ft.: 2,873
Bonus Sq. Ft: 552
Bedrooms: 3   Bathrooms: 2½
Foundation: Crawl space standard; slab for an additional fee
See index on page 95 for more information

Optional Second Floor 552 sq. ft.

First Floor 2,873 sq. ft.

call toll-free 1-800-373-2646   houseplansandmore.com

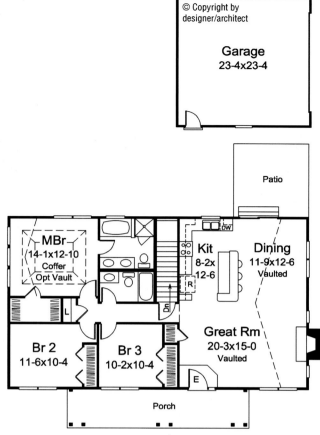

Plan #900-121D-0025

Images provided by designer/architect

Dimensions: 50' W x 34'6" D
Heated Sq. Ft.: 1,368
Bedrooms: 3   Bathrooms: 2
Foundation: Basement standard; crawl space or slab for an additional fee
See index on page 95 for more information

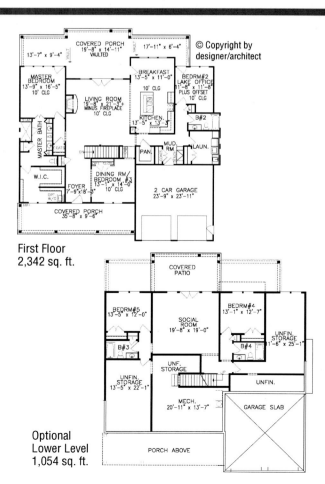

Plan #900-056D-0137

Images provided by designer/architect

Dimensions: 62'10" W x 68'5" D
Heated Sq. Ft.: 2,342
Bonus Sq. Ft.: 1,054
Bedrooms: 3   Bathrooms: 2
Foundation: Basement
See index on page 95 for more information

Plan #900-161D-0022

Dimensions: 104'10" W x 93'10" D
Heated Sq. Ft.: 3,338
Bedrooms: 3   Bathrooms: 3½
Exterior Walls: 2" x 6"
Foundation: Crawl space

See index on page 95 for more information

Images provided by designer/architect

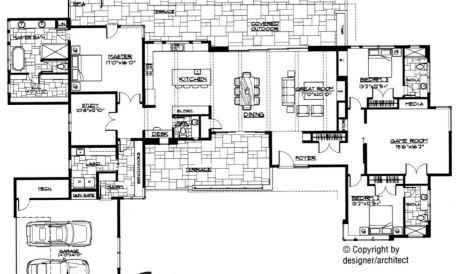

© Copyright by designer/architect

Features

- The perfect open floor plan for today's family focuses on plenty of windows and private bedrooms for every family member
- A massive great room, dining area, and kitchen form the main hub of this home
- A private master suite has a sun-filled bath with a free-standing tub and separate shower
- 3-car side entry garage

Plan #900-011D-0347

Dimensions: 113'4" W x 62'8" D
Heated Sq. Ft.: 2,910
Bedrooms: 3   Bathrooms: 3
Exterior Walls: 2" x 6"
Foundation: Post & beam or joisted continuous footings standard; slab or basement for an additional fee
See index on page 95 for more information

Images provided by designer/architect

Features

- The foyer has 11' ceilings with wood columns into the vaulted great room straight ahead for an open and rustic interior
- The vaulted great room has gorgeous exposed beams, and a fireplace with built-ins
- An open floor plan combines the great room, kitchen, and dining room into one big "family triangle," with no walls to cramp the space
- The kitchen has an island with a double sink, 10' ceilings, and plenty of counterspace
- 3-car side entry garage

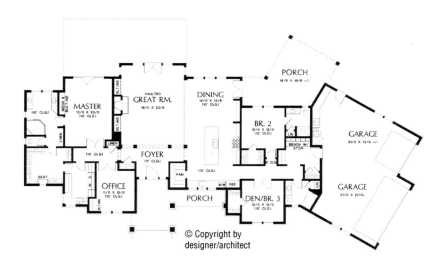

© Copyright by designer/architect

x

Plan #900-167D-0006

Dimensions: 68'11" W x 69'10" D
Heated Sq. Ft.:   2,939
Bedrooms: 4   Bathrooms: 3½
Exterior Walls: 2" x 6"
Foundation: Slab standard; crawl space
for an additional fee
See index on page 95 for more information

Images provided by designer/architect

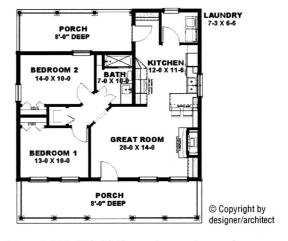

Images provided by designer/architect

Plan #900-028D-0109

Dimensions: 33' W x 40' D
Heated Sq. Ft.:   890
Bedrooms: 2   Bathrooms: 1
Exterior Walls: 2" x 6"
Foundation: Crawl space or slab,
please specify when ordering
See index on page 95 for more information

© Copyright by
designer/architect

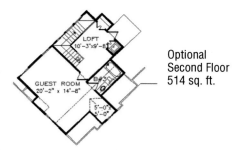

Optional
Second Floor
514 sq. ft.

Images provided by designer/architect

Plan #900-056D-0108

Dimensions: 102'4" W x 74' D
Heated Sq. Ft.: 2,803
Bonus Sq. Ft.: 514
Bedrooms: 3   Bathrooms: 2½
Foundation: Slab standard; crawl space
or basement for an additional fee
See index on page 95 for more information

© Copyright by
designer/architect

First Floor
2,803 sq. ft.

Plan #900-086D-0143

Images provided by designer/architect

Dimensions: 45' W x 55' D
Heated Sq. Ft.: 1,562
Bedrooms: 3   Bathrooms: 2
Foundation: Basement
See index on page 95 for more information

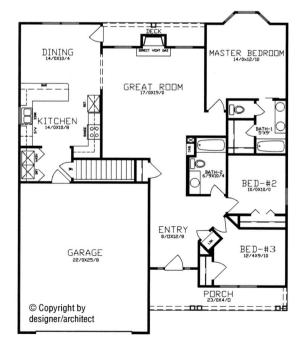

© Copyright by
designer/architect

Plan #900-155D-0047

Dimensions: 60' W x 80'4" D
Heated Sq. Ft.: 2,500
Bonus Sq. Ft.: 354
Bedrooms: 3   Bathrooms: 2½
Foundation: Slab or crawl space,
please specify when ordering
See index on page 95 for more information

Features

- Modern farmhouse touches grace the interior of this attractive rustic-looking ranch home

- The vaulted great room has a centered fireplace directly across from the island in the kitchen creating an intimate and cozy feel

- The master suite boasts a bath with a free-standing tub, a separate shower, a double-sink vanity, and a huge walk-in closet with built-ins

- Two additional bedrooms share a full bath

- The optional second floor has an additional 354 square feet of living area

- 2-car front entry garage

call toll-free 1-800-373-2646   houseplansandmore.com

Alternate Slab
or
Crawl Space
Layout

Images provided by designer/architect

Plan #900-001D-0024

Dimensions: 68' W x 38' D
Heated Sq. Ft.:   1,360
Bedrooms: 3   Bathrooms: 2
Foundation: Basement standard; crawl space or slab for an additional fee
See index on page 95 for more information

Images provided by designer/architect

Plan #900-157D-0015

Dimensions: 62' W x 74'4" D
Heated Sq. Ft.:   2,620
Bonus Sq. Ft.:   438
Bedrooms: 3   Bathrooms: 2½
Foundation: Crawl space standard; slab for an additional fee
See index on page 95 for more information

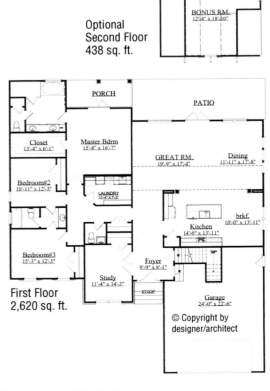

Optional
Second Floor
438 sq. ft.

First Floor
2,620 sq. ft.

Plan #900-007D-0124

Dimensions: 65' W x 51' D
Heated Sq. Ft.:   1,944
Bedrooms: 3   Bathrooms: 2
Foundation: Basement standard; crawl
space or slab for an additional fee
See index on page 95 for more information

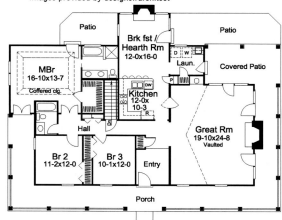

Detached Garage
34-4x23-4

Plan #900-166D-0001

Dimensions: 49'5" W x 84'9" D
Heated Sq. Ft.:   2,232
Bedrooms: 2   Bathrooms: 2½
Exterior Walls: 2" x 6"
Foundation: Slab
See index on page 95 for more information

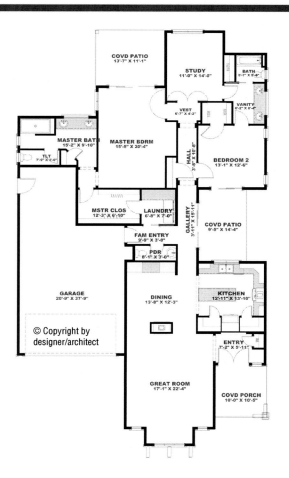

Plan #900-101D-0052

Dimensions:	129'8" W x 70'8" D
Heated Sq. Ft.:	2,611
Bonus Sq. Ft.:	2,456
Bedrooms: 2	Bathrooms: 2½
Exterior Walls:	2" x 6"
Foundation:	Walk-out basement

See index on page 95 for more information

Features

- Open living Craftsman home with barrier free living spaces
- An angled den off the of foyer creates a private home office
- There is a convenient mud room and laundry area as you enter from the garage
- The master bedroom has a pampering bath with an oversized walk-in closet
- The optional lower level has an additional 2,456 square feet of living area with two bedrooms, a game nook, a theater, a recreation area, an exercise room, and a vault
- 3-car front entry garage

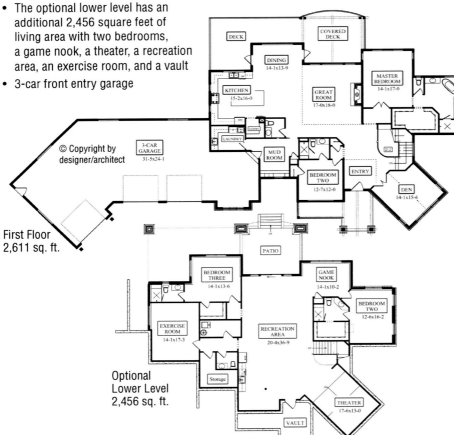

First Floor
2,611 sq. ft.

Optional
Lower Level
2,456 sq. ft.

Images provided by designer/architect

bonus rooms & basements
finding flexibility within your home

You found it – the perfect dream home! It has the exact number of bedrooms and bathrooms. The open floor plan is great. The kitchen is spacious, the mud room ideal, and the storage is awesome. You even have a bonus room. Now, what to do with that space? Here lies the beauty of this space – you can do whatever you like! From newlyweds to families of five, the bonus room holds numerous possibilities for every homeowner to customize their design as they see fit. Many one-story homes today are designed with bonus or flex spaces that give families that wiggle room when additional space is needed. Let your imagination run wild! There are so many opportunities to make this your area for fun, fitness, work or relaxation; you name it.

Think Big

Maximize your home's fun quotient by finishing your flex or bonus space for a big time fun spot everyone will love! Better yet, your basement may be below ground, but there's nothing sub-par about these ideas!

here are a few favorites

the playroom

Every mom wishes she had a place where she could put those extra toys, keeping them from clashing with her living room décor, or ending up under her feet while she tries to fix dinner. So why not put that bonus room to good use as a designated playroom? Organizational systems of cubbies, baskets, and shelves will keep an unruly collection of toys organized, while providing enough space to enjoy playing with them. Bean bag chairs and play rugs in bright colors keep the room fun and functional. You could even break the room down into stations — an art area with chalkboard paint walls for your budding Van Gogh, a reading corner with special pillows and lighting, or a block table for the young architect. Keep this room child-friendly and fun and your kids will flock there, all while keeping the mess out of the rest of the house.

the home theater

To turn your bonus room into your own personal theater experience, you need surprisingly few items. A quality television (a smart TV is even better), proper media players, and surround sound are the best setup. Now that your theater is functional it's time to personalize your movie watching experience. Are you going to put in oversized reclining chairs and couches, or movie theater seats? Will you put in dimming ambient lights? How about a popcorn machine? After all, the primary reason you have a home theater is to enjoy cinema entertainment in unsurpassed comfort. Some homeowners with serious theater systems choose to have professional input and installation. Whether home designed or professionally outfitted, the home theater is a bonus room design enjoyed by all.

the family gathering spot

Often called a recreation or game room, this family gathering spot is the place where family can get together and relax. Filled with games, movies, and perhaps a snack area or wet bar, this bonus room is great for families that need an informal space to hang out in that doesn't necessarily need to be kept perfect like the highly visible great room. Keep this space cozy and inviting for making family memories.

the home gym

We all know someone who has purchased home workout equipment only to realize that the plan was not thought out. Bulky equipment is a pain to set up and take down everyday, so it often goes unused. If the equipment is left out, those machines always manage to take up awkward amounts of space. Even small free weights often find themselves in the way, causing stubbed toes and storage woes. Turning your bonus room into a home gym, or exercise room creates a designated space for all that equipment, plus it allows options of customized flooring or built-in sound systems. It will definitely make exercising less of a chore since you won't have to leave the house!

the home office

If you choose to work from home, there is no more valuable a space than a bonus room that's been turned into a home office. Remember that your home office is a reflection of you and the work you produce. Make it a priority to keep the space efficient and eye-appealing with necessary storage, noise buffers, and organizational systems. Keeping this room working for you makes working from home a pleasant experience and ensures the bonus room is never a wasted space.

double your square footage **+** customize your basement **=** something special

many of today's one-story homes like the ones featured in this book are designed with an optional lower level. Offering flexibility if additional square footage is needed or desired, finishing a lower level can instantly increase a home's square footage providing added bedrooms, gathering space, or whatever you need to make your home more functional and work for you. Gone are the days of a home's basement being only used as a place for old boxes. The basements, or lower levels of today are nothing in comparison. Basement storage is being transformed into finished family spaces. The most popular options are best broken into specialized areas. From gaming to movie theaters, much like a bonus or flex room, your basement can be designed to your unique desires.

need more ideas?

game on

What you do with your dedicated game room depends on the game to be played. Families may choose to have a special table for game play, with shelves installed to organize their extensive board game collections. Poker, or Texas Hold'em are popular and if you love to play, then a personalized table, chips, and cards would be great additions to this space. Pool tables, air hockey, shuffleboard, and even full-scale arcade games are also available for purchase, allowing fans to recreate their favorite gaming experiences – without worrying about their high scores being challenged!

make the most of media

As family life becomes more hectic, free time spent together is often wanted at home. The availability of flat screen smart televisions, surround sound (often wireless), and multiple video, audio, gaming systems and apps allow any media experience to be enjoyed at full capacity without ever leaving home. Specialized lighting can add the appropriate ambiance when movie watching or having gaming tournaments with just a click of the remote.

lounging around

For some families, extra space is best outfitted with the amenities needed to relax. Cozy furniture, warm lighting, blankets and bookshelves create a desirable place to retreat to while enjoying one another's company.

Many families choose to mix and match the different suggestions, creating zones of activity within the basement. Additionally, refreshment centers are becoming more popular in finished basements, adding to the level of comfort. These can be uniquely designed, ranging from full-scale kitchens to specialized wet bars. Wine cellars and humidors are also popular in many households. Keep in mind that with refreshments usually come bathrooms. Full baths, saunas, hot tubs, and even guest rooms are prevalent in basements when resources allow.

When it comes to decorating and creating a specific atmosphere, it may be best to consider a theme. This works particularly well for dedicated rooms. If you are choosing to outfit your basement for multiple uses, stick to something that will be enjoyed by everyone without overshadowing any particular area. Your basement is one more opportunity to show how creative you are – so, don't hold back!

Attempt to use as much of the space as you can. Vertical shelves are great for visible, neat storage, while also giving you further places to display pictures and other treasures while also promoting a feeling of spaciousness with their height.

hit the floor

Flooring is important, and the basement will likely be exposed to heavy traffic flow. Durability and comfort are both vital in addition to stain resistance and sound proofing. Cork flooring is growing in popularity for these reasons. Another popular choice is luxury vinyl laminate, or ceramic tile. Both options can look exactly like stone or wood flooring, but are entirely waterproof, perfect for damp environments like basements and areas where there will be plenty of entertaining and a chance for frequent spills.

let there be light

Recessed lighting eliminates overhead and keeps from wasting floor space, but it can be expensive. Sconces are another idea to prevent wasting precious space, but try to include as much natural light as possible to avoid the feeling of being underground. Today, many areas

have code requirements for egress windows in basements, these windows are larger than their traditional counterparts and allow much more natural light to filter into a space. They alleviate the feeling of a dark, damp basement instantly, and they also allow any bedroom designed in the basement space to be considered a true bedroom when you plan to resell your home. Per code, a bedroom must have a proper escape method if there's a fire, and an egress window is large enough for just that.

make it multi-task

Some homeowners like the idea of multiple uses but really desire the peace of reading a book without overhearing the poker game going on across the room. Don't give up the hope of having both a flexible and functional recreation room. Curtain rails and bi-fold doors/walls can be installed. Section off areas in use or open up a room to its greatest space potential, perfect for privacy or parties.

As you ponder finishing your basement whether it's a game room, or a tranquil spa and meditation area, keep in mind the space allowed as well as your budget, time constrictions and future needs. Measure the area and plan for traffic flow and adequate seating. It will be beneficial to pick a large space and plot the exact layout you desire. Homeowners are often surprised to find that a simple ping-pong table can take up a third of a room's floor space when unfolded. It is essential to have a defined plan for what amenities you want to include in your new basement, in addition to where they will be located. Then, discuss your desires with your contractor. They can re-evaluate, and ensure the design is feasible. Although tempting, avoid purchasing items until your contractor has agreed to a layout. If you already own specific items, inform your contractor of their existence so those components are not eliminated when adjustments occur. With a little creativity, your former damp, dark basement will become the family's favorite gathering place, or the much-needed comfortable guest or living quarters you've always wanted and needed.

Plan #900-011D-0640

Dimensions: 58' W x 62' D
Heated Sq. Ft.:   1,834
Bedrooms: 3   Bathrooms: 2
Exterior Walls: 2" x 6"
Foundation: Joisted crawl space
standard; slab or basement for an
additional fee

See index on page 95 for more information

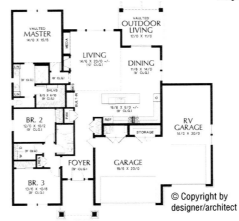

© Copyright by
designer/architect

Plan #900-077D-0019

Dimensions: 54' W x 47' D
Heated Sq. Ft.:   1,400
Bedrooms: 3   Bathrooms: 2
Foundation: Slab, basement or crawl
space, please specify when ordering
See index on page 95 for more information

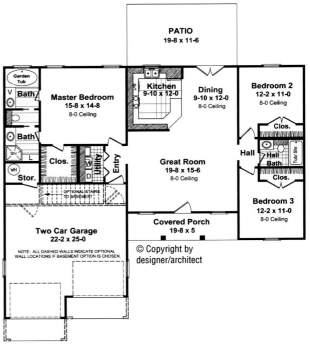

© Copyright by
designer/architect

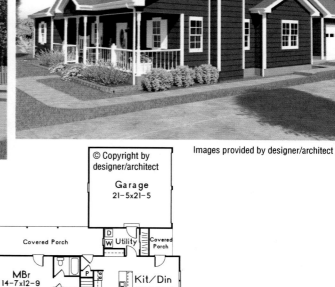

Images provided by designer/architect

Plan #900-001D-0031

Dimensions: 48' W x 66' D
Heated Sq. Ft.:   1,501
Bedrooms: 3   Bathrooms: 2
Foundation: Basement standard; crawl
space or slab for an additional fee
See index on page 95 for more information

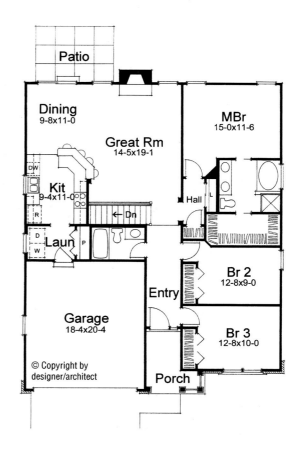

Plan #900-147D-0001

Images provided by designer/architect

Dimensions: 40'8" W x 49'4" D
Heated Sq. Ft.:   1,472
Bedrooms: 3   Bathrooms: 2
Foundation: Basement, crawl space or
slab, please specify when ordering
See index on page 95 for more information

Plan #900-101D-0077

Dimensions:	68' W x 77' D
Heated Sq. Ft.:	2,422
Bonus Sq. Ft.:	1,491
Bedrooms: 2	Bathrooms: 2½
Exterior Walls:	2" x 6"

Foundation: Basement or daylight basement, please specify when ordering

See index on page 95 for more information

Features

- Rustic ranch living has been achieved in this beautiful home
- The kitchen enjoys a massive island that overlooks the great room and dining area
- The master bedroom is tucked away nicely and includes a huge walk-in shower, and an oversized walk-in closet in its private bath
- The spacious mud room/laundry will keep everyone organized
- The optional lower level has an additional 1,491 square feet of living area and includes two additional bedrooms, a family room with wet bar, and an exercise room
- 2-car side entry garage and 1-car front entry garage

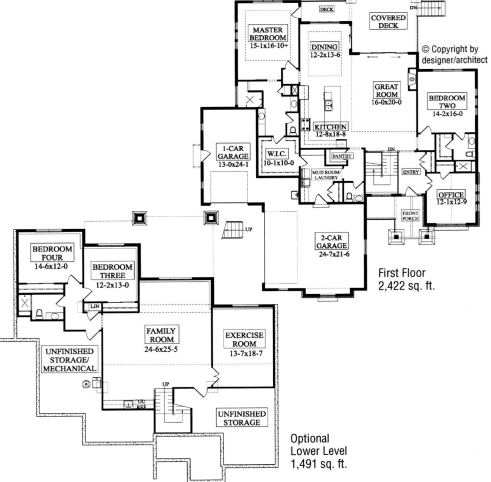

© Copyright by designer/architect

First Floor
2,422 sq. ft.

Optional
Lower Level
1,491 sq. ft.

call toll-free 1-800-373-2646   houseplansandmore.com

Plan #900-051D-0974

Dimensions:	60' W x 73' D
Heated Sq. Ft.:	1,736
Bedrooms: 2	Bathrooms: 2
Exterior Walls:	2" x 6"

Foundation: Basement standard; crawl space or slab for an additional fee

See index on page 95 for more information

Images provided by designer/architect

Features

- A deep Craftsman style porch greets all those who enter this home and has enough space for a swing or rocking chairs

- The ever-popular open floor plan reigns in this home featuring sunny dining and great rooms with a kitchen overlooking it all

- The kitchen has a unique and functional hidden pantry that seamlessly blends with the rest of the cabinets

- The super-private master bedroom enjoys a spacious walk-in closet extending from the bath

- 3-car front entry garage

CVRD. PORCH
17'0"x14'0"
DECK

DIN. RM.
13'0"x12'6"

GRT. RM.
16'8"x19'4"

MBR.
14'6"x13'8"

KIT.
15'8"x11'0"

HIDDEN
PANTRY

LOCKERS

BR. #2
13'4"x10'6"

E.

3 CAR GARAGE
35'4"x25'4"

© Copyright by
designer/architect

Plan #900-101D-0045

Dimensions:	69' W x 68'3" D
Heated Sq. Ft.:	1,885
Bedrooms: 2	Bathrooms: 2½
Exterior Walls:	2" x 6"
Foundation:	Basement

See index on page 95 for more information

Images provided by designer/architect

Features

- The open floor plan maximizes space creating a flowing open layout
- A dual fireplace warms the family room as well as the outdoor covered patio
- The spacious and private master suite includes its own bath and walk-in closet
- Guests will never want to leave the guest bedroom with its own bath and large walk-in closet
- 3-car front entry garage

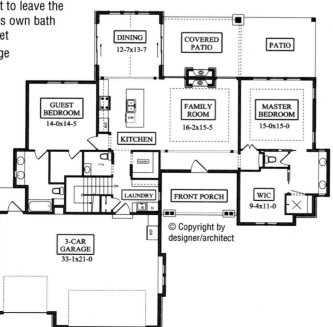

© Copyright by designer/architect

Images provided by designer/architect

Plan #900-007D-0113

Dimensions: 66' W x 66' D
Heated Sq. Ft.:   2,547
Bedrooms: 4   Bathrooms: 2½
Foundation: Basement

See index on page 95 for more information

Patio

MBr
14-8x17-0

Br 2
11-0x12-0

Great Room
19-0x20-2
(12' clg.)

Brk'ft
(12' clg.)

Kitchen
21-8x19-9
(12' clg.)

Hall

Laundry

Br 3
12-0x11-0

Hall

Entry

Dn

Dining
12-4x15-6
tray clg.

Br 4 /
Study
12-0x14-0

Porch

Garage
21-4x29-4

© Copyright by
designer/architect

Images provided by designer/architect

Plan #900-032D-0826

Dimensions: 41'4" W x 38'4" D
Heated Sq. Ft.:   1,313
Bedrooms: 2   Bathrooms: 1
Exterior Walls: 2" x 6"
Foundation: Basement standard; crawl
space, floating slab or monolithic slab
for an additional fee

See index on page 95 for more information

10'-0" x 12'-8"

11'-0" x 11'-8"

10'-0" x 12'-8"

17'-0" x 14'-0"

14'-0" x 12'-0"

© Copyright by
designer/architect

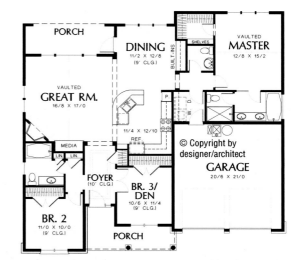

Plan #900-011D-0007

Dimensions: 50' W x 48' D
Heated Sq. Ft.: 1,580
Bedrooms: 3   Bathrooms: 2½
Exterior Walls: 2" x 6"
Foundation: Joisted crawl space,
TrusJoist floor system or post & beam
standard; slab or basement for an
additional fee
See index on page 95 for more information

Plan #900-016D-0062

Dimensions: 48' W x 43'4" D
Heated Sq. Ft.: 1,380
Bonus Sq. Ft: 385
Bedrooms: 3   Bathrooms: 2
Foundation: Slab or crawl space
standard; basement or walk-out
basement for an additional fee
See index on page 95 for more information

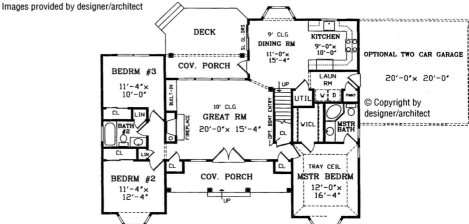

Plan #900-055D-0748

Dimensions: 67'2" W x 55'10" D
Heated Sq. Ft.:   2,525
Bedrooms: 4   Bathrooms: 3
Foundation: Crawl space or slab standard; basement or walk-out basement for an additional fee
See index on page 95 for more information

Images provided by designer/architect

Features

- This expansive one-story design has the split-bedroom floor plan everyone loves
- Stunning columns frame the foyer that leads into the open great room with fireplace
- The formal dining room, casual breakfast room, and large grilling porch with fireplace provide an abundance of locations for dining opportunities
- 2-car front entry garage

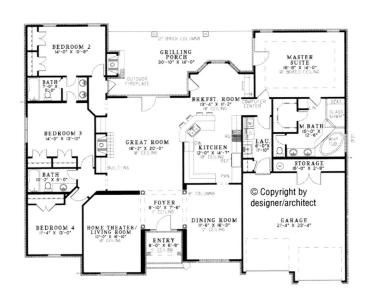

Plan #900-011S-0018

Dimensions: 77' W x 65' D
Heated Sq. Ft.: 4,600
Bedrooms: 4   Bathrooms: 3½
Exterior Walls: 2" x 6"
Foundation: Partial crawl space/
walk-out basement
See index on page 95 for more information

Features

- A totally unique glass floor leads to the staircase and allows one to look down to the lower level below
- Plant shelves adorn this house in numerous places creating an airy, outdoorsy feel
- The differently designed kitchen has most of its emphasis on a gracious center island
- The master bedroom flows into an open bathroom with a spa tub and a double-bowl vanity
- 3-car front entry tandem garage

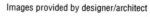

Images provided by designer/architect

First Floor
2,624 sq. ft.

© Copyright by designer/architect

Lower Level
1,976 sq. ft.

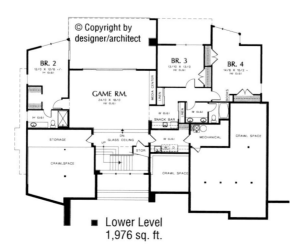

Plan #900-101D-0059

Dimensions: 88'6" x W 67'6" D
Heated Sq. Ft.: 2,196
Bonus Sq. Ft.: 1,517
Bedrooms: 2   Bathrooms: 2
Exterior Walls: 2" x 6"
Foundation: Basement, daylight basement or walk-out basement, please specify when ordering
See index on page 95 for more information

Images provided by designer/architect

Features

- This home was designed with 10' ceilings on both the first floor and the lower level making it extremely open and spacious

- The laundry and mud room merge to form a powerhouse of efficiency and organization including lockers, a closet, and extra counterspace

- The L-shaped kitchen island offers plenty of seating and houses a double sink and the dishwasher

- The optional lower level has an additional 1,517 square feet of living area and includes three additional bedrooms, two baths, an exercise room, and a large recreation area with a wet bar

- 2-car front entry, 1-car side entry garage

© Copyright by designer/architect

First Floor
2,196 sq. ft.

Optional
Lower Level
1,517 sq. ft.

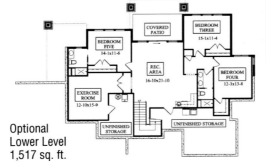

Plan #900-011D-0342

Dimensions:	63' W x 61'6" D
Heated Sq. Ft.:	2,368
Bedrooms: 3	Bathrooms: 2½
Exterior Walls:	2" x 6"

Foundation: Joisted crawl space or post & beam standard; slab or basement for an additional fee
See index on page 95 for more information

Images provided by designer/architect

Features

- This Craftsman home's curb appeal will make it a standout in any neighborhood with its tasteful combination of stone, siding and multiple gables
- The chef of the family will love the island in the kitchen, the walk-in pantry, and the spacious snack bar space
- The nearby laundry room is bright and cheerful, with plenty of counterspace for folding clothes
- The secluded office could serve as a guest room, or a place for hobbies
- The well-appointed master suite features a vaulted ceiling, and a lovely window arrangement with transoms above that overlooks the backyard
- A sit-down shower anchors the posh master bath, which also includes a toilet space, dual sinks and a walk-in closet
- 3-car front entry garage

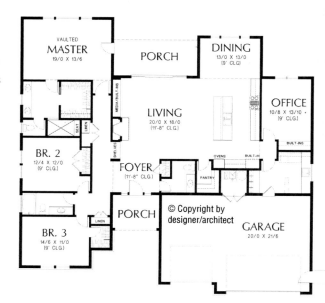

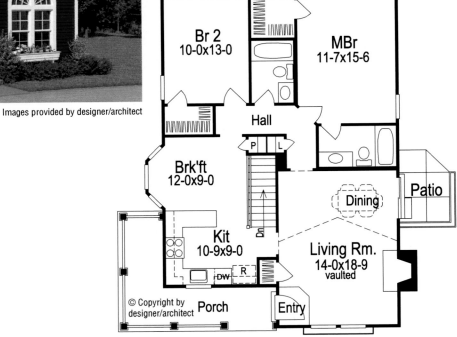

Plan #900-007D-0105

Dimensions: 35' W x 40'8" D
Heated Sq. Ft.:   1,084
Bedrooms: 2   Bathrooms: 2
Foundation: Basement standard; crawl
space for an additional fee
See index on page 95 for more information

Floor plan labels:
- Br 2 10-0x13-0
- MBr 11-7x15-6
- Hall
- Brk'ft 12-0x9-0
- Kit 10-9x9-0
- Dining
- Patio
- Living Rm. 14-0x18-9 vaulted
- Porch
- Entry

© Copyright by designer/architect

Plan #900-026D-2071

Dimensions: 57'8" W x 58' D
Heated Sq. Ft.:   1,925
Bedrooms: 3   Bathrooms: 2
Exterior Walls: 2" x 6"
Foundation: Basement standard; crawl
space, slab or walk-out basement for
an additional fee
See index on page 95 for more information

Floor plan labels:
- Dining Area 19⁸ x 11⁸
- Great Room 16⁵ x 19⁰ 10'-0" CEILING
- Kit 13⁰ x 11⁸
- Owner's Suite 13⁰ x 15⁴ 10'-0" CEILING
- Br.2 12⁰ x 10¹⁰
- Br.3 11⁸ x 10¹⁰
- Pocket Office 11⁸ x 6⁷
- Garage 21⁴ x 21⁸
- Covered Porch

© Copyright by designer/architect

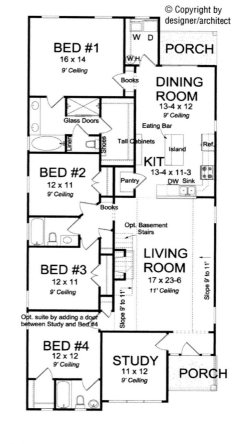

Floor plan labels:

BED #1
16 x 14
9' Ceiling

PORCH

W D

W.H.

Books

DINING ROOM
13-4 x 12
9' Ceiling

Glass Doors

Liner

Shoes

Eating Bar

Tall Cabinets

Island

Ref.

KIT
13-4 x 11-3

BED #2
12 x 11
9' Ceiling

Pantry

DW   Sink

Books

BED #3
12 x 11
9' Ceiling

Opt. Basement Stairs

LIVING ROOM
17 x 23-6
11' Ceiling

Slope 9' to 11'   Slope 9' to 11'

Opt. suite by adding a door between Study and Bed #4

BED #4
12 x 12
9' Ceiling

STUDY
11 x 12
9' Ceiling

PORCH

Plan #900-130D-0344

Images provided by designer/architect

Dimensions: 32' W x 70' D
Heated Sq. Ft.:   2,062
Bedrooms: 4   Bathrooms: 3
Foundation: Slab standard; crawl space
or basement for an additional fee
See index on page 95 for more information

Images provided by designer/architect

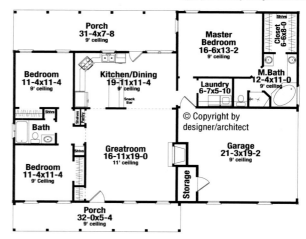

Floor plan labels:

Porch
31-4x7-8
9' ceiling

Master Bedroom
16-6x13-2
9' ceiling

Closet
6-6x8-0

Bedroom
11-4x11-4
9' ceiling

Kitchen/Dining
19-11x11-4
9' ceiling

Snack Bar

M.Bath
12-4x11-0
9' ceiling

Laundry
6-7x5-10

Bath

Greatroom
16-11x19-0
11' ceiling

Garage
21-3x19-2
9' ceiling

Bedroom
11-4x11-4
9' Ceiling

Storage

Porch
32-0x5-4
9' ceiling

Plan #900-084D-0016

Dimensions: 56' W x 45'8" D
Heated Sq. Ft.:   1,492
Bedrooms: 3   Bathrooms: 2
Foundation: Slab standard; crawl space
or basement for an additional fee
See index on page 95 for more information

Plan #900-161D-0024

Dimensions:	114' W x 93'6" D
Heated Sq. Ft.:	3,665
Bedrooms: 3	Bathrooms: 3½
Exterior Walls:	2" x 6"
Foundation:	Crawl space

See index on page 95 for more information

Images provided by designer/architect

Features

- Stunning modern sensibility offers limitless interior spaces and smart function in this beautiful home
- A great layout has two bedrooms in one wing, each with their own bath, and a game room tucked between them
- The kitchen is wide open to all activities in the great room and dining area
- The master suite enjoys a private spa courtyard, terrace access, a posh private bath, and massive walk-in closet
- Everyone will be jealous of the mud room which has a large bench with hooks, a powder room, a built-in desk, and laundry room access
- 3 car side entry garage

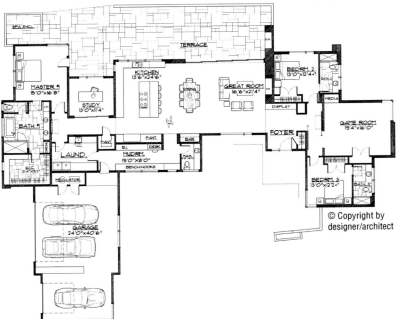

© Copyright by designer/architect

Plan #900-007D-0140

Dimensions: 62' W x 45' D
Heated Sq. Ft.: 1,591
Bedrooms: 3   Bathrooms: 2
Foundation: Basement standard; crawl space or slab for an additional fee

See index on page 95 for more information

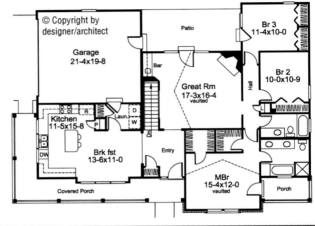

Plan #900-167D-0001

Dimensions: 59'6" W x 60' D
Heated Sq. Ft.: 2,017
Bedrooms: 3   Bathrooms: 3
Exterior Walls: 2" x 6"
Foundation: Crawl space standard; slab for an additional fee

See index on page 95 for more information

Images provided by designer/architect

Plan #900-056D-0090

Dimensions: 92'1" W x 83'4" D
Heated Sq. Ft.: 2,767
Bedrooms: 3   Bathrooms: 2½
Foundation: Slab standard; crawl space for an additional fee

See index on page 95 for more information

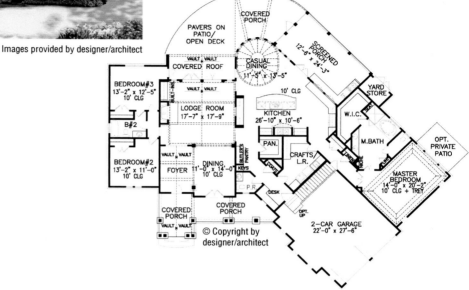

© Copyright by designer/architect

Images provided by designer/architect

Plan #900-011D-0006

Dimensions: 70' W x 51' D
Heated Sq. Ft.: 1,873
Bedrooms: 3   Bathrooms: 2
Exterior Walls: 2" x 6"
Foundation: Joisted crawl space, post & beam, or TrusJoist floor system standard; slab or basement for an additional fee

See index on page 95 for more information

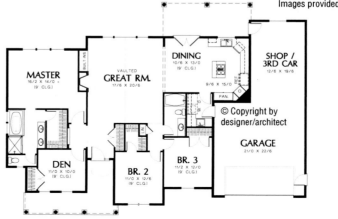

© Copyright by designer/architect

Plan #900-055S-0036

Dimensions:	89' W x 104' D
Heated Sq. Ft.:	4,121
Bonus Sq. Ft.:	1,826
Bedrooms: 3	Bathrooms: 3

Foundation: Slab or crawl space standard; basement or daylight basement for an additional fee

See index on page 95 for more information

Images provided by designer/architect

Features

- An 11' boxed ceiling, a media center, a wet bar, and a cozy corner fireplace make the hearth room/den the center of activity

- The master suite is full of amenities including a corner fireplace, a luxury bath, an exercise room, and a unique reinforced storm closet for shelter

- An immense home theater or game room and bonus room on the second floor provide an additional 1,826 square feet of living space for entertaining and fun for the whole family

- 3-car side entry garage

Optional Second Floor 1,826 sq. ft.

© Copyright by designer/architect

First Floor 4,121 sq. ft.

Plan #900-084D-0086

Dimensions: 45'4" W x 76' D
Heated Sq. Ft.: 1,725
Bedrooms: 3   Bathrooms: 2
Foundation: Slab standard; crawl space
for an additional fee
See index on page 95 for more information

Images provided by designer/architect

Features

- This stylish ranch home offers a great split bedroom layout for a more narrow lot
- The open living area enjoys beautiful views of the outdoor living space that features an outdoor fireplace
- The kitchen enjoys a snack bar, a center work island, tons of storage floor-to-ceiling and even a built-in desk
- A cheerful dining area is surrounded in windows
- The private master bedroom features a luxury bath with two walk-in closets, a double-bowl vanity, an oversized tub and walk-in easy access shower
- 2-car front entry garage

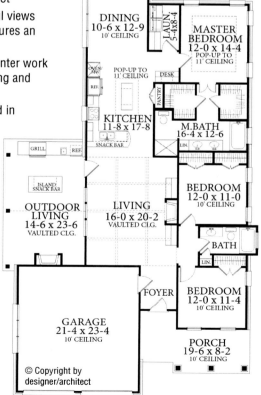

Plan #900-007D-0134

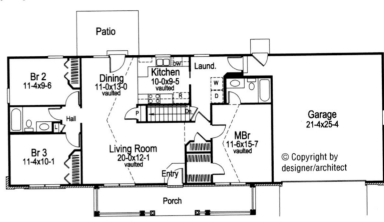

Images provided by designer/architect

Dimensions: 73'8" W x 32' D
Heated Sq. Ft.: 1,310
Bedrooms: 3   Bathrooms: 2
Foundation: Basement standard; crawl space or slab for an additional fee
See index on page 95 for more information

Plan #900-121D-0036

Images provided by designer/architect

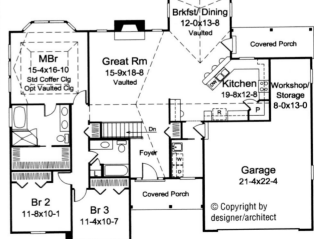

Dimensions: 60'4" W x 52' D
Heated Sq. Ft.: 1,820
Bedrooms: 3   Bathrooms: 2
Foundation: Basement standard; crawl space or slab for an additional fee
See index on page 95 for more information

Plan #900-013D-0235

Dimensions: 71'2" W x 64'6" D
Heated Sq. Ft.: 2,140
Bonus Sq. Ft.: 1,535
Bedrooms: 3   Bathrooms: 3
Foundation: Crawl space standard;
basement or slab for an additional fee
See index on page 95 for more information

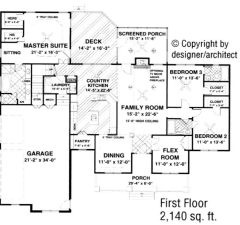

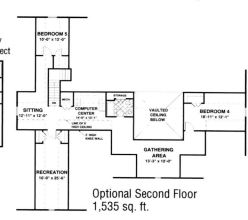

First Floor
2,140 sq. ft.

Optional Second Floor
1,535 sq. ft.

Plan #900-001D-0067

Dimensions: 48' W x 37'8" D
Heated Sq. Ft.: 1,285
Bedrooms: 3   Bathrooms: 2
Foundation: Crawl space standard;
basement or slab for an additional fee
See index on page 95 for more information

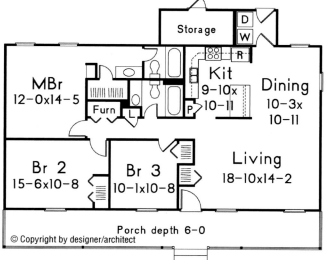

Images provided by designer/architect

Plan #900-101D-0057

Dimensions:	58' W x 90' D
Heated Sq. Ft.:	2,037
Bonus Sq. Ft.:	1,330
Bedrooms: 1	Bathrooms: 1½
Exterior Walls:	2" x 6"
Foundation:	Walk-out basement

See index on page 95 for more information

Features

- This home has two levels of covered patios and decks
- The entry hall is flanked by the formal dining room and a staircase to the lower level
- The U-shaped kitchen has dining space and a wet bar
- The master bedroom is in a private wing and features a stepped ceiling, a luxurious bath, and a large walk-in closet
- The optional lower level has an additional 1,330 square feet of living area and offers two bedrooms with baths, an office, a recreation area, and a safe room
- 3-car side entry garage

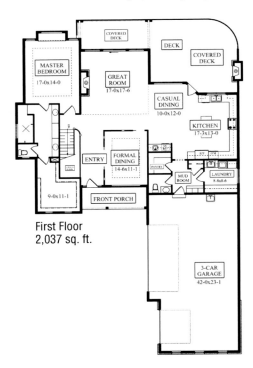

First Floor
2,037 sq. ft.

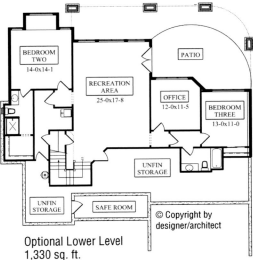

© Copyright by designer/architect

Optional Lower Level
1,330 sq. ft.

call toll-free 1-800-373-2646   houseplansandmore.com

Plan #900-007D-0055

Dimensions: 67' W x 51'4" D
Heated Sq. Ft.: 2,029
Bedrooms: 3   Bathrooms: 2
Foundation: Basement standard; crawl space or slab for an additional fee
See index on page 95 for more information

Features

- The kitchen enjoys extravagant cabinetry and counterspace in a bay, island snack bar, built-in pantry and cheerful dining area with multiple tall windows

- An angled staircase descends from the large entry with wood columns and is open to a vaulted great room with a corner fireplace

- A lovely master bedroom boasts two walk-in closets, a private bath with double-door entry, and a secluded porch

- 2-car side entry garage

Plan #900-032D-1081

Dimensions: 50' W x 38' D
Heated Sq. Ft.:   1,604
Bedrooms: 2   Bathrooms: 2
Exterior Walls: 2" x 6"
Foundation: Basement standard; crawl
space, floating slab or monolithic slab
for an additional fee

See index on page 95 for more information

© Copyright by
designer/architect

Plan #900-007D-0049

Dimensions: 68' W x 48'4" D
Heated Sq. Ft.:   1,791
Bedrooms: 4   Bathrooms: 2
Foundation: Basement standard; crawl
space or slab for an additional fee

See index on page 95 for more information

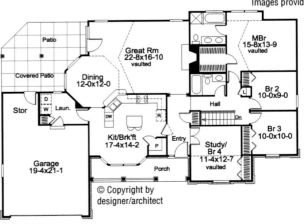

© Copyright by
designer/architect

call toll-free 1-800-373-2646   houseplansandmore.com

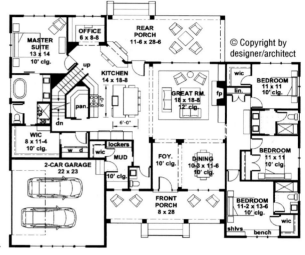

Plan #900-091D-0523

Dimensions: 69' W x 57'6" D
Heated Sq. Ft.: 2,514
Bonus Sq. Ft.: 390
Bedrooms: 4   Bathrooms: 3½
Exterior Walls: 2" x 6"
Foundation: Basement standard; crawl space or slab for an additional fee
See index on page 95 for more information

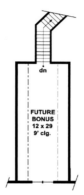

Optional Second Floor 390 sq. ft.

FUTURE BONUS 12 x 29 9' clg.

dn

First Floor 2,514 sq. ft.

Floor plan labels:
MASTER SUITE 13 x 14 10' clg.
OFFICE 6 x 8-8
REAR PORCH 11-6 28-6
KITCHEN 14 x 18-8
up
GREAT RM. 18 x 18-8 12' clg.
fp
BEDROOM 11 x 11 10' clg.
pan.
6'-0"
dn
wic
lin.
WIC 8 x 11-4 10' clg.
lockers
w d
MUD
BEDROOM 11 x 11 10' clg.
2-CAR GARAGE 22 x 23
10' clg.
FOY. 10' clg.
DINING 10-3 x 11-6 10' clg.
FRONT PORCH 8 x 28
BEDROOM 11-2 x 13-6 10' clg.
wic
shlvs
bench

Plan #900-024D-0824

Dimensions: 61'9" W x 89'9" D
Heated Sq. Ft.: 3,224
Bonus Sq. Ft.: 238
Bedrooms: 4   Bathrooms: 3
Foundation: Floating slab
See index on page 95 for more information

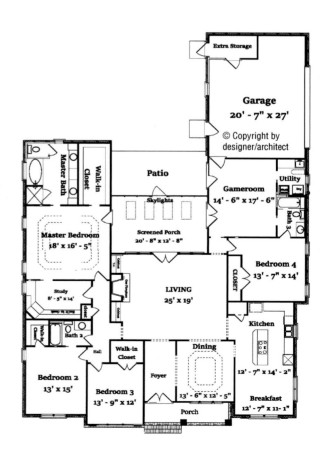

Floor plan labels:
Extra Storage
Garage 20' - 7" x 27'
Master Bath
Walk-in Closet
Patio
Skylights
Gameroom 14' - 6" x 17' - 6"
Utility
Bath 3
Master Bedroom 18' x 16' - 5"
Screened Porch 20' - 8" x 12' - 8"
Bedroom 4 13' - 7" x 14'
CLOSET
Study 8' - 5" x 14'
LIVING 25' x 19'
Bath 2
Kitchen 12' - 7" x 14' - 2"
Walk-in Closet
Hall
Walk-in Closet
Dining 13' - 6" x 12' - 5"
Foyer
Bedroom 2 13' x 15'
Bedroom 3 13' - 9" x 12'
Porch
Breakfast 12' - 7" x 11' - 1"

Plan #900-051D-0985

Dimensions: 70'6" W x 78' D
Heated Sq. Ft.: 2,510
Bedrooms: 3   Bathrooms: 2½
Exterior Walls: 2" x 6"
Foundation: Basement standard; crawl space or slab for an additional fee
See index on page 95 for more information

Features

- Some great extras can be found throughout this floor plan including a private den off the dining room, and a private computer nook

- There is a laundry room as well as a mud room with built-in lockers for keeping everyone organized

- The kitchen features a large island with great room views and a corner walk-in pantry

- The master bedroom enjoys its privacy and has a luxury bath, and two sizable walk-in closets

- 3-car side entry garage

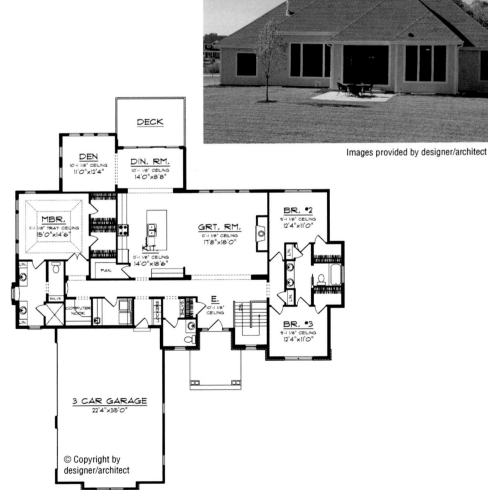

Images provided by designer/architect

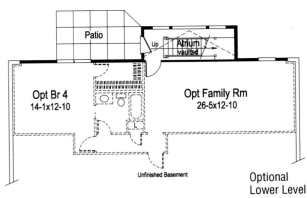

Patio

Up

Atrium
vaulted

Opt Br 4
14-1x12-10

Opt Family Rm
26-5x12-10

Unfinished Basement

Optional
Lower Level
740 sq. ft.

Plan #900-007D-0136

Dimensions:	71'8" W x 38' D
Heated Sq. Ft.:	1,532
Bonus Sq. Ft.:	740
Bedrooms: 3	Bathrooms: 2
Foundation:	Walk-out basement

See index on page 95 for more information

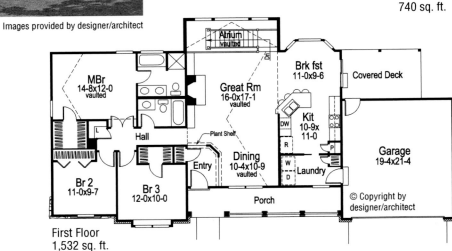

Atrium
vaulted

MBr
14-8x12-0
vaulted

Great Rm
16-0x17-1
vaulted

Brk fst
11-0x9-6

Covered Deck

Hall

Plant Shelf

Kit
10-9x
11-0

Br 2
11-0x9-7

Br 3
12-0x10-0

Entry

Dining
10-4x10-9
vaulted

Laundry

Garage
19-4x21-4

Porch

© Copyright by
designer/architect

First Floor
1,532 sq. ft.

Plan #900-055D-0193

Dimensions:	63'10" W x 72'2" D
Heated Sq. Ft.:	2,131
Bedrooms: 3	Bathrooms: 2½

Foundation: Slab or crawl space
standard; basement or daylight
basement for an additional fee

See index on page 95 for more information

GRILLING
PATIO
13'-4" X 12'-0"

GAS
BBQ

SCREENED
PORCH
29'-8" X 12'-0"

MASTER
SUITE
13'-0" X 17'-2"

GREAT RM.
18'-0" X 22'-0"

DINING
13'-8" X 13'-8"

M.BATH
15'-0" X 17'-4"

VAULTED
CEILING

SKYLIGHTS

VAULTED
CEILING

BATH

COMPUTER
CENTER

KITCHEN
12'-10" X 10'-6"

RANGE
W/ MW

REF

FRENCH
DOORS

PANTRY

WINDOW
SEAT

BEDROOM 2
14'-8" X 12'-6"

BEDROOM 3 /
DEN
13'-6" X 14'-2"

FOYER
7'-7" X 11'-10"

STORM
SHELTER

LAU.
8'-7" X 7'-8"

KID'S
NOOK
BENCH /
HANGING

DN

OPTIONAL BASEMENT PLAN

GARAGE
21'-0" X 27'-4"

© Copyright by designer/architect

COVERED PORCH
36'-8" X 8'-0"

call toll-free 1-800-373-2646   houseplansandmore.com

Plan #900-077D-0043

Dimensions: 64' W x 45'10" D
Heated Sq. Ft.: 1,751
Bedrooms: 3   Bathrooms: 2
Foundation: Slab, basement or crawl space, please specify when ordering
See index on page 95 for more information

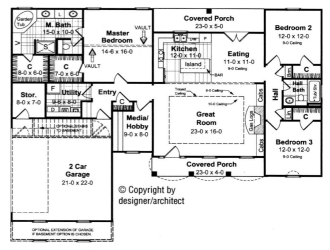

© Copyright by designer/architect

Plan #900-011D-0660

Dimensions: 52' W x 53' D
Heated Sq. Ft.: 1,704
Bedrooms: 3   Bathrooms: 2½
Exterior Walls: 2" x 6"
Foundation: Joisted continuous footings or post & beam standard; slab for an additional fee
See index on page 95 for more information

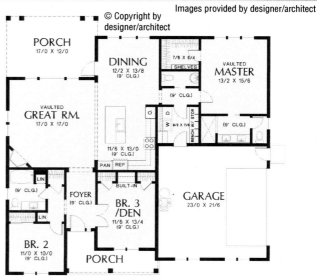

© Copyright by designer/architect

Plan #900-139D-0047

Dimensions:	73' W x 81'3" D
Heated Sq. Ft.:	4,086
Bedrooms: 4	Bathrooms: 4
Exterior Walls:	2" x 6"

Foundation: Walk-out basement standard; crawl space, slab or daylight basement for an additional fee

See index on page 95 for more information

Features

- This country home offers an amazing layout for families with its split bedroom floor plan
- The kitchen features a breakfast area and an island
- The office is near the front entry and has built-ins on one wall
- Neat transom windows adorn the shared bath
- 3-car side entry garage

Images provided by designer/architect

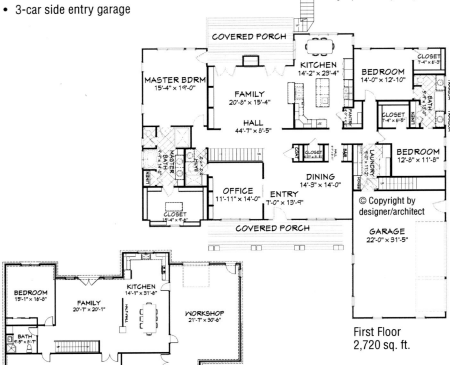

© Copyright by designer/architect

First Floor
2,720 sq. ft.

Lower Level
1,366 sq. ft.

Plan #900-101D-0056

Dimensions:	72' W x 77' D
Heated Sq. Ft.:	2,593
Bonus Sq. Ft.:	1,892
Bedrooms: 2	Bathrooms: 2½
Exterior Walls:	2" x 6"
Foundation:	Walk-out basement

See index on page 95 for more information

Images provided by designer/architect

Features

- This stunning home has the look and feel homeowners love with its sleek interior and wide, open floor plan

- The great room, kitchen and dining area combine maximizing the square footage and making these spaces functional and comfortable

- The master bedroom enjoys a first floor private location adding convenience for the homeowners and it includes an oversized walk-in closet, and a private bath with a walk-in shower, a free-standing tub, and a double-bowl vanity

- The optional lower level has an additional 1,892 square feet of living area and adds extra amenities like a media area, a billiards room, a rec room, and an exercise room in addition to two additional bedrooms and two full baths

- 3-car front entry garage

First Floor
2,593 sq. ft.

© Copyright by designer/architect

Optional
Lower Level
1,892 sq. ft.

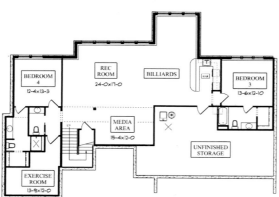

Plan #900-033D-0012

Dimensions: 60' W x 43' D
Heated Sq. Ft.:   1,546
Bedrooms: 3   Bathrooms: 2
Foundation: Basement

See index on page 95 for more information

Images provided by designer/architect

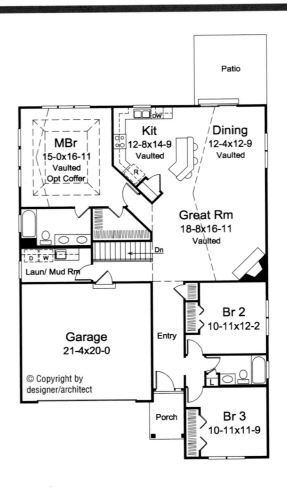

Br 2
10-6x12-0

Great Rm
13-10x14-6
vaulted

Dinette
11-2x10-2
vaulted

MBr
14-0x14-10

Kit
11-2x13-2
vaulted

Br 3
10-11x10-8

Dining
10-4x 12-8
vaulted

Porch

Garage
20-0x22-0

© Copyright by
designer/architect

Plan #900-121D-0023

Dimensions: 41' W x 60'4" D
Heated Sq. Ft.:   1,762
Bedrooms: 3   Bathrooms: 2
Foundation: Basement standard; crawl
space or slab for an additional fee

See index on page 95 for more information

Images provided by designer/architect

Patio

MBr
15-0x16-11
Vaulted
Opt Coffer

Kit
12-8x14-9
Vaulted

Dining
12-4x12-9
Vaulted

Great Rm
18-8x16-11
Vaulted

Laun/ Mud Rm

Dn

Garage
21-4x20-0

Entry

Br 2
10-11x12-2

© Copyright by
designer/architect

Porch

Br 3
10-11x11-9

call toll-free 1-800-373-2646   houseplansandmore.com

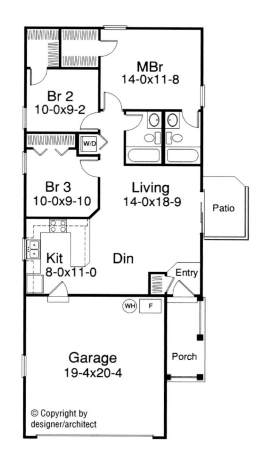

Plan #900-007D-0108

Dimensions: 25' W x 60' D
Heated Sq. Ft.:   983
Bedrooms: 3   Bathrooms: 2
Foundation: Crawl space standard; slab
for an additional fee

See index on page 95 for more information

Floor plan labels:
- MBr 14-0x11-8
- Br 2 10-0x9-2
- Br 3 10-0x9-10
- Living 14-0x18-9
- Patio
- Kit 8-0x11-0
- Din
- Entry
- W/D
- WH / F
- Garage 19-4x20-4
- Porch

Plan #900-026D-2029

Dimensions: 52'8" W x 56' D
Heated Sq. Ft.:   1,595
Bedrooms: 2   Bathrooms: 2
Exterior Walls: 2" x 6"
Foundation: Slab standard; basement,
crawl space or walk-out basement for
an additional fee

See index on page 95 for more information

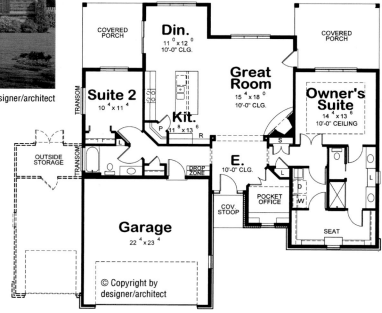

Floor plan labels:
- COVERED PORCH
- Din. 11-0 x 12-0 10'-0" CLG.
- COVERED PORCH
- Great Room 15-4 x 18-0 10'-0" CLG.
- Owner's Suite 14-4 x 13-6 10'-0" CEILING
- Suite 2 10-4 x 11-4
- Kit. 11-8 x 13-6
- E. 10'-0" CLG.
- OUTSIDE STORAGE
- TRANSOM
- DROP ZONE
- POCKET OFFICE
- COV. STOOP
- SEAT
- Garage 22-4 x 23-4

the *Social* kitchen

You have just put the finishing touches on a beautiful table centerpiece, and on the spread of hors d'oeuvres and other delectable culinary treats for your gathering. The utmost attention to detail has been made to the great room, dining area, and all of the gathering places in your home. You want to make sure your guests feel pampered, comfortable, and completely at ease. But, no matter how inviting your great room may be, why does it always seem everyone ends up gathering in the kitchen?

Kitchens seem to be magnets for everyone who enters a home. Maybe it's the flurry of activity always taking place there, or the scrumptious aromas that fill the air making guests want to investigate what possibly could be cooking. Whatever the reason, kitchens are everyone's favorite gathering spots in the home. So, instead of fighting it, give in and make your kitchen a socially inviting place that is comfortable, fun, and also allows you to get everything done even if people are lingering about. There are many ways to create social spots that keep everyone in the kitchen, while allowing him or her to feel welcome and comfortable in participating in the activities.

Thankfully, today's floor plans are taking this into consideration now more than ever. Most homes being designed today utilize an open floor plan that easily integrates the kitchen into the gathering spaces seamlessly. So, no longer is the kitchen hidden behind a swinging door. It's actually a stunning focal point filled with many design elements that enhance the entire gathering area including seating, dining space and other amenities. The kitchen is the center of your home; where you do the most work, where you entertain friends, where you gather as a family, and where life happens. It is hands-down the busiest area of the home and needs to be carefully planned for function as well as style.

Unless noted, copyright by designer/architect; Page 84 top: Plan #026D-1891, Crown V Photography LLC; bottom: Plan #032D-0667; Page 85 top: Kohler Crevasse sink, kohler.com; Plan #900-101D-0093 on page 90, Diggles Creative, Warren Diggles, photographer; Plan #032D-0427; Plan #900-101D-0052 on page 44, Damon Searles, photographer; See additional photos and purchase plans at houseplansandmore.com.

A home's kitchen tends to be a place that quickly turns into a dumping ground. With the daily mail, homework projects, laundry, food storage and office work finding its way there, the kitchen can often have an identity crisis since there are so many different activities being carried out in the same space. Well, these habits will never change most likely, so instead of letting them aggravate you, embrace them and learn how to incorporate all of your family's favorite activities into this one wonderful place within your home.

One way to create an inviting place with function within your kitchen is to create a chopping and chatting spot. Whether it's a breakfast bar counter, an island, work-bench or table, guests and family will need a spot that can function as a place for dining, prepping a meal, or finishing the homework that's due tomorrow. A decent space for gathering around will become a beacon and will keep everyone right where the action is, but out of the cooking space. An important thing to remember when creating this special gathering spot is that you don't want to crowd your kitchen with too many tables, or an island that is too oversized. It shouldn't affect the natural traffic flow, or act as a barrier. Pick a piece of furniture, or a space that facilitates function, storage, and possibly workspace, plus a spot where people feel they can just hang out and not be in the chef's way.

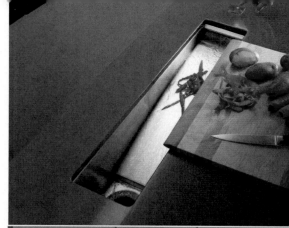

Another important factor to include when creating a social kitchen is to make sure there is plenty of seating. Use stools, benches and other seating options to offer plenty of places for your guest to "pop a squat." Of course, you may be thinking that your dining table has chairs and that should be enough, but think of other types of seating that can be tucked away (under a counter, for example) and can remain out of sight. That is also why the idea of a bench is great. It can provide a handy place to drop things the minute you come in the door, plus when company arrive, it's an instant spot for chatting with the chef. Everyone enjoys gathering in the kitchen and enjoying chips and dip, while watching the cook finish up meal time tasks. Having comfortable stools, benches, and other seating options ensures your guests are comfortable. Even better, stick with wood, plastic or other low-maintenance options for this seating and if spills occur, clean up will be a breeze.

Adding a variety of lighting in the kitchen is another way to make this space feel inviting, warm and comfortable for all those who enter it. Add lighting under the cabinets, recessed lighting in the ceiling, over tables and work zones so that all the bases are covered. That way, when the family cozies up around the table playing games, you can just light the table area and its nearby surroundings for a warmer feel. Plus, light sources can really play with the mood of the space.

When entertaining, use soft lighting, and when cooking or prepping, turn up the lighting so it's safer for everyone involved with the tasks at hand. Even soft candlelight adds warmth and dimension to a space making it feel intimate and less institutional.

A great inexpensive way to change the amount of light in your kitchen is to install dimmer switches on light sources. That way, the light above the sink can be bright enough for kitchen tasks at mealtime and then turned down much lower and used as a night light after everyone has gone off to bed. Dimmers allow great versatility and keep you from having an overabundance of lighting that may make your kitchen feel too busy, distracting or tense.

A kitchen filled entirely of glass cabinetry would be a little distressing don't you think? With all those kitchen gadgets being seen by everyone who came into the space, all of the clutter would make for a busy space that would be unnerving for most. But, strategically placing a

couple of glass front cabinets in your kitchen can really become a focal point. If you have a great collection of brightly colored vases or old-fashioned pitchers, glass front cabinets give you the perfect opportunity to display away. Not only will they add some great character to your kitchen interior, but they will surely become conversation starters.

Just remember that less is more. Select just a few key items to be seen in these cabinets and avoid the temptation of showing a huge collection. It will make your kitchen instantly cluttered and less interesting than just giving them a glimpse of your special collection.

Making some minor adjustments with the layout, seating options, lighting, and cabinetry can add scores of points when family and guests gather in your kitchen. Instead of trying to find ways to keep everyone out while you cook away, invite them in and let the party begin

your dream kitchen wish list

If you're designing the ultimate kitchen, trying to make your kitchen more functional for entertaining, or building a new home and trying to remember the things to take into consideration with a kitchen layout, it is important to remember that it is one of the best home investments you can make so make sure it meets all your needs right from the start.

The three main appliances in the kitchen are the sink, the refrigerator, and the stove. Make sure you arrange them so the workspace flows.

sink or swim
Of the three appliances, the sink gets the most use. Place it in an area of the kitchen that is visually appealing to its user. So, don't push it up against a wall without a view. Place it in front of a window with a view to the outdoors, or in an island that overlooks the other areas of the home. It is also important to place the dishwasher to either side of the sink so that loading dishes is convenient. Many kitchens have a second sink, one for preparing food and another for dishes. Some kitchens also feature a second dishwasher, one for gently washing breakables and another for power scrubbing pots and pans.

shut the fridge
When it comes to the refrigerator there are many basic options such as brand, color, size and finish. But, also think about the various styles including a freezer/fridge combination, side-by-side doors, a top and bottom door style, a style with an ice and water dispenser in the door, a smart fridge with technology that allows you to see what's inside it from your smart phone, and now the fun retro refrigerators meant to make a bold decorating statement and be a focal point. Also showing resurgence, refrigerators with the same cabinet style treatment added to the door so they don't stand out in your kitchen, are becoming quite popular again. Shiny stainless steel finishes are becoming less popular as the new appliances being introduced have a matte finish. Whatever option you choose make sure you leave plenty of room for the doors to open completely. If the fridge is placed near a wall make sure the doors and drawers open freely without hitting the wall. It is a good idea to check with the manufacturer for specific installation dimensions. And, becoming extremely popular especially if a kitchen is small are counter the depth refrigerators. These slightly smaller sized models offer a seamless look to your kitchen that feels custom since the appliance doesn't stick out further than the countertops. It easily adds square footage to your kitchen without it being obvious.

too hot in the kitchen
The options available for stoves go way beyond gas or electric. There are cooktops, double ovens, oven and microwave combinations, burners and griddle tops, convection and even warming drawers. When making a decision it is important to think about the type of cooking you plan to do and how much space you have to work with. The cooking surface needs to be planned to allow for workspace that is easily accessible and safe.

The selection process isn't over just yet...now, it's time to think about cabinets, shelving, countertops, pantry units, closets, a planning center, electronics, a center island, and eating space!

cabinets, shelving & countertops
You can never have too much storage and this is especially true in the kitchen with all of the gadgets that need to be stored. Most common are cabinets with closed fronts, but also available are open cabinets where plates are stored on end and open fronts where objects are quickly within reach. It is a good idea to consider cabinets that go to the ceiling. The top shelf can easily be reached with a step stool and can hold items not used on a daily basis. Countertops need to be durable and accent the cabinetry. There can be built-in items such as cutting boards and seamless sinks. There are many surfaces available and the biggest decision will be how long you want it to last and how much you want to spend. Granite has long been a favorite, but new homeowners are also opting for quartz, concrete, or recycled glass countertops.

pantries, storage walls & closets
Pantries are a great way to store all food in one place. They are wider than a standard cabinet and have additional storage shelves. If space allows, a built-in pantry closet is a wonderful addition to a kitchen. They can be placed in the general vicinity of the kitchen and custom shelving added to meet your storage needs. Storage walls in kitchens are very popular too, and typically linger in the area near the stove. Often shelves are mounted on a wall near the stove and include spices, measuring cups, oils, vinegars and other cooking essentials. Or, kitchen storage walls are found on another wall often floor-to-ceiling and have an assortment of china, ceramic bowls, glassware and other items that look nice displayed together. Both decorative and functional, these kitchen walls can really show off your personality, while providing the extra storage always needed in the kitchen.

planning & technology centers

Growing in popularity, the planning or technology center is basically a simplified "home office" located in the kitchen or adjacent to it. It can consist of a desk with surrounding cabinets and storage, space for a computer or ipad®, a charging station with additional USB ports, an area to organize bills and other important papers, cubbies or bins for every family member to stay organized, and a family schedule.

kitchen electronics

There are so many items that are used in the kitchen that need to be plugged in, make sure there are plenty of electrical outlets so you don't have to run extension cords. Mockett® simplifies the need for electrical outlets everywhere in the kitchen with the pop-up kitchen outlet design (see below). Simply, click it and it ascends from the countertops to reveal additional outlets that can be used when additional seldom used appliances are needed.

kitchen island

An island in the kitchen can function as an eating bar, additional workspace, or can house the cooktop or sink. Whatever the function, it usually ends up being the focal point of the kitchen and can be accented with dramatic lighting, or hanging kitchen racks that will creatively hold your pots and pans while reclaiming valuable cabinet space. Designing it with different colors than the other cabinets and countertops is a popular trend and makes it even more of a focal point.

eating space

This can be a nook, breakfast bar, banquette or island and for many families on the go it is where most of the meals are served. If you plan on having an eat-in kitchen, make sure there is enough stools so everyone has a place to sit.

If you're trying to design or plan the layout of a new kitchen the options are a little overwhelming, but it is important to remember that it needs to be well-organized and efficient, as well as beautiful since it is everyone's favorite spot. After all, it is the place you live, entertain and most importantly – cook! From cabinetry to appliances, it is important to create the perfect gathering space so that the chef, as well as family and friends, are always happy when they enter.

Unless noted, copyright by designer/architect; Page 86, Plan #082S-0004; Page 87 top: Plan #900-101D-0052 on page 44, Damon Searles, photographer; left: Do-It-Yourself Decorative Charging Box, centsationalgirl.com; left: Plan #026D-1891, Crown V Photography, LLC; above: Mockett® Convenience Kitchen Outlet, Item #PCS39/EE/HW, mockett.com; See additional photos and purchase plans at houseplansandmore.com.

First Floor
1,415 sq. ft.

Atrium

Dining Area

Kit
10-2x
11-9

Garage
22-0x11-9

© Copyright by designer/architect

Great Rm
18-0x21-8
vaulted

Laun.

Entry

Porch

Hall

Br 2
11-4x12-6

MBr
12-8x15-0

Shelves

Vaulted

Vaulted

Patio

Up

Family Rm
25-0x21-4

Unexcavated

Lower Level
507 sq. ft.

Unfinished Basement

Plan #900-007D-0068

Dimensions:	55'8" W x 46'4" D
Heated Sq. Ft.:	1,922
Bedrooms: 2	Bathrooms: 2
Foundation:	Walk-out basement

See index on page 95 for more information

Images provided by designer/architect

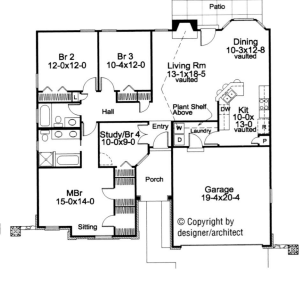

Images provided by designer/architect

Plan #900-007D-0162

Dimensions:	47'8" W x 47'4" D
Heated Sq. Ft.:	1,519
Bedrooms: 4	Bathrooms: 2

Foundation: Crawl space standard; basement or slab for an additional fee
See index on page 95 for more information

Patio

Br 2
12-0x12-0

Br 3
10-4x12-0

Living Rm
13-1x18-5
vaulted

Dining
10-3x12-8
vaulted

Hall

Plant Shelf Above

Kit
10-0x
13-0
vaulted

Study/Br 4
10-0x9-0

Entry

Laundry

MBr
15-0x14-0

Porch

Garage
19-4x20-4

Sitting

© Copyright by designer/architect

Plan #900-076D-0231

Dimensions: 69'4" W x 67'7" D
Heated Sq. Ft.: 2,467
Bonus Sq. Ft: 447
Bedrooms: 3   Bathrooms: 2½
Foundation: Crawl space or slab, please
specify when ordering

See index on page 95 for more information

First Floor
2,467 sq. ft.

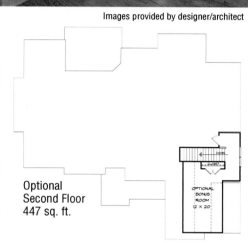

Optional
Second Floor
447 sq. ft.

Images provided by designer/architect

© Copyright by
designer/architect

Plan #900-167D-0007

Dimensions: 72' W x 76'9" D
Heated Sq. Ft.: 3,016
Bedrooms: 4   Bathrooms: 3
Exterior Walls: 2" x 6"
Foundation: Slab standard; crawl space
for an additional fee

See index on page 95 for more information

Images provided by designer/architect

© Copyright by
designer/architect

Plan #900-101D-0093

Dimensions:	76'9" W x 70'6" D
Heated Sq. Ft.:	2,615
Bonus Sq. Ft:	2,274
Bedrooms: 2	Bathrooms: 2½
Exterior Walls:	2" x 6"
Foundation:	Basement

See index on page 95 for more information

Images provided by designer/architect

Features

- An open kitchen is surrounded by gathering spaces including a hearth room, and a great room
- There is a designated home office space near the master bedroom
- The mud room features a walk-in closet, a bench, and cubbies creating plenty of extra storage
- The optional lower level has an additional 2,274 square feet of living area including two additional bedrooms, a living room, billiards with a wet bar, a home theater and even a Lego® room
- 3-car front entry garage

© Copyright by designer/architect

Optional Lower Level
2,274 sq. ft.

First Floor
2,615 sq. ft.

Plan #900-101D-0108

Dimensions: 87'6" W x 86' D
Heated Sq. Ft.: 2,744
Bonus Sq. Ft: 1,869
Bedrooms: 2   Bathrooms: 2½
Exterior Walls: 2" x 6"
Foundation: Basement, daylight basement or walk-out basement, please specify when ordering

See index on page 95 for more information

Images provided by designer/architect

Features

- The kitchen has a large island with dining space that looks over the vaulted great room
- A private first floor guest room has its own covered deck, walk-in closet and private bath making it ideal as an in-law suite
- The mud room provides plenty of storage for great organization
- The optional lower level has an additional 1,869 square feet of living area and includes a rec area, a wet bar, two guest bedrooms, an exercise room, a sauna plus two full baths
- 2-car front side garage and 1-car front entry garage

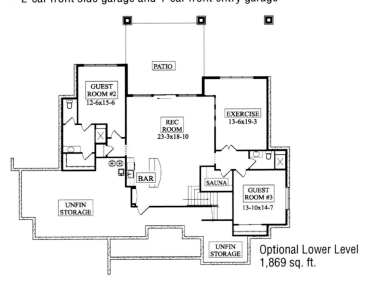

Optional Lower Level
1,869 sq. ft.

First Floor
2,744 sq. ft.

© Copyright by designer/architect

Plan #900-055D-1039

Dimensions: 91'6" W x 61'3" D
Heated Sq. Ft.: 2,688
Bonus Sq. Ft.: 602
Bedrooms: 4   Bathrooms: 3½
Foundation: Crawl space or slab standard; basement or daylight basement for an additional fee
See index on page 95 for more information

Features

- This stunning ranch home has a two-story vaulted and beamed ceiling in the great room and kitchen
- The outdoor living/grilling porch is adorned with a fireplace for extending your outdoor time into the colder months
- The master suite enjoys a private location and has a huge walk-in shower in the private bath
- The optional second floor has an additional 602 square feet of living area
- 2-car side entry garage and 1-car front entry garage

Optional Second Floor 602 sq. ft.

Images provided by designer/architect

© Copyright by designer/architect

First Floor 2,688 sq. ft.

Plan #900-121D-0016

Dimensions: 42'4" W x 54' D
Heated Sq. Ft.: 1,582
Bedrooms: 3   Bathrooms: 2
Foundation: Basement standard; crawl space or slab for an additional fee
See index on page 95 for more information

Features

- The covered front porch is perfect for relaxing and enjoying the outdoors
- Vaulted ceilings throughout this home provide an open and airy atmosphere
- The kitchen boasts a large walk-in pantry and ample counterspace with an eating bar for convenient meals
- 2-car front entry detached garage

Images provided by designer/architect

Detached Garage
23-4x23-4

© Copyright by designer/architect

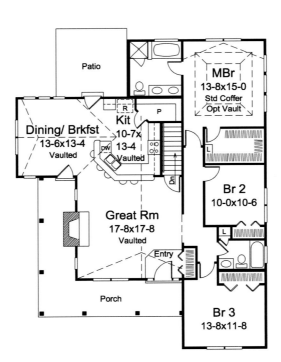

Patio

MBr
13-8x15-0
Std Coffer
Opt Vault

Dining/ Brkfst
13-6x13-4
Vaulted

Kit
10-7x
13-4
Vaulted

Br 2
10-0x10-6

Great Rm
17-8x17-8
Vaulted

Entry

Porch

Br 3
13-8x11-8

HOME PLAN INDEX

PLEASE NOTE: Plan pricing shown below is subject to change without notice. For current pricing, all available plan packages and options, visit houseplansandmore.com, or call 1-800-373-2646.

Plan Number	Square Feet	PDF File	5-Sets	CAD File	Material List	Page
900-001D-0024	1,360	$889	$889	$1,389	$125	42
900-001D-0031	1,501	$989	$989	$1,589	$125	51
900-001D-0067	1,285	$889	$889	$1,389	$125	71
900-005D-0001	1,400	$889	$889	$1,389	$125	34
900-007D-0010	1,845	$989	$989	$1,589	$125	14
900-007D-0049	1,791	$989	$989	$1,589	$125	74
900-007D-0055	2,029	$1,089	$1,089	$1,789	$125	73
900-007D-0060	1,268	$889	$889	$1,389	$125	20
900-007D-0068	1,922	$989	$989	$1,589	$125	88
900-007D-0105	1,084	$789	$789	$1,239	$125	62
900-007D-0108	983	$789	$789	$1,239	$125	83
900-007D-0113	2,547	$1,189	$1,189	$1,989	$125	56
900-007D-0124	1,944	$989	$989	$1,589	$125	43
900-007D-0134	1,310	$889	$889	$1,389	$125	70
900-007D-0136	1,532	$989	$989	$1,589	$125	78
900-007D-0140	1,591	$989	$989	$1,589	$125	66
900-007D-0146	1,929	$989	$989	$1,589	$125	27
900-007D-0162	1,519	$989	$989	$1,589	$125	88
900-007D-5060	1,344	$889	$889	$1,389	-	27
900-011D-0006	1,873	$1,263	$1,438	$2,526	$170	67
900-011D-0007	1,580	$1,119	$1,294	$2,238	$170	57
900-011D-0224	1,802	$1,208	$1,383	$2,416	$170	28
900-011D-0229	2,904	$1,580	$1,755	$3,160	$170	17
900-011D-0342	2,368	$1,430	$1,605	$2,860	$170	61
900-011D-0347	2,910	$1,619	$1,794	$3,238	$170	374
900-011D-0637	1,744	$1,217	$1,392	$2,434	$170	26
900-011D-0640	1,834	$1,239	$1,414	$2,478	$170	50
900-011D-0660	1,704	$1,213	$1,388	$2,426	$170	79
900-011S-0018	4,600	$2,147	$2,322	$4,294	$220	59
900-011S-0101	3,296	$1,770	$1,945	$3,540	$170	18
900-013D-0230	1,800	$1,045	$1,145	$1,595	$195	23
900-013D-0235	2,140	$1,195	$1,245	$1,695	$195	71
900-016D-0049	1,793	$965	$1,015	$1,895	$95	15
900-016D-0062	1,380	$840	$890	$1,695	$95	57
900-024D-0824	3,224	$1,612	-	$1,612	-	75
900-026D-2029	1,595	$935	-	$1,636	-	83
900-026D-2071	1,925	$975	-	$1,706	$125	62
900-028D-0099	1,320	$745	$870	-	-	14
900-028D-0109	890	$695	$770	-	-	38
900-032D-0826	1,313	$950	$900	$1,630	$140	56
900-032D-0930	1,676	$1,080	$1,040	$1,770	$160	21
900-032D-1081	1,604	$1,020	$970	$1,700	$150	74
900-033D-0012	1,546	$1,510	$850	-	-	82
900-051D-0960	2,784	$1,352	$1,081	$2,162	-	10
900-051D-0972	1,490	$1,107	$882	$1,744	-	29
900-051D-0974	1,736	$1,148	$918	$1,811	-	54
900-051D-0981	2,005	$1,234	$979	$1,953	-	22
900-051D-0985	2,510	$1,316	$1,046	$2,091	-	76
900-055D-0193	2,131	$1,100	$1,200	$2,200	-	78
900-055D-0748	2,525	$1,100	$1,200	$2,200	-	58
900-055D-1039	2,688	$1,550	$1,650	$3,100	-	93
900-055S-0036	4,121	$1,550	$1,650	$3,100	-	68
900-056D-0090	2,767	$2,495	-	$3,445	-	67
900-056D-0108	2,803	$2,495	-	$3,445	-	39
900-056D-0122	1,338	$1,195	-	$2,045	-	29
900-056D-0137	2,342	$1,495	-	$2,445	-	35
900-056S-0019	3,480	$2,795	-	$3,845	-	33
900-065D-0426	1,718	$875	$925	$1,320	$75	28
900-076D-0220	3,061	$1,950	$1,200	$2,600	-	12
900-076D-0231	2,467	$1,600	$995	$2,100	-	89
900-077D-0019	1,400	$1,300	$1,200	$1,725	$150	50
900-077D-0043	1,751	$1,425	$1,325	$1,850	$150	79
900-077D-0259	1,870	$1,425	$1,325	$1,850	$150	21
900-084D-0016	1,492	$950	$995	$1,850	$65	63
900-084D-0086	1,725	$1,050	$1,090	$1,950	-	69
900-086D-0143	1,562	$989	$989	$1,589	-	39
900-091D-0510	2,125	$2,040	$1,719	$2,723	-	20
900-091D-0523	2,514	$2,040	$1,719	$2,723	-	75
900-101D-0045	1,885	$1,250	-	$2,350	-	55
900-101D-0052	2,611	$1,400	-	$2,650	-	44
900-101D-0056	2,593	$1,400	-	$2,650	-	81
900-101D-0057	2,037	$1,250	-	$2,350	-	72
900-101D-0059	2,196	$1,250	-	$2,350	-	60
900-101D-0077	2,422	$1,400	-	$2,650	-	52
900-101D-0089	2,509	$1,400	-	$2,650	-	25
900-101D-0093	2,615	$1,400	-	$2,650	-	90
900-101D-0094	2,650	$1,400	-	$2,650	-	30
900-101D-0108	2,744	$1,600	-	$2,900	-	92
900-121D-0016	1,582	$989	$989	$1,589	$125	94
900-121D-0023	1,762	$989	$989	$1,589	$125	82
900-121D-0025	1,368	$889	$889	$1,389	$125	35
900-121D-0036	1,820	$989	$989	$1,589	$125	70
900-130D-0344	2,062	$1,025	-	$1,320	-	63
900-139D-0047	4,086	$1,495	$1,620	$2,995	-	80
900-141D-0143	1,340	$906	$944	$1,531	-	15
900-147D-0001	1,472	$889	$889	-	-	51
900-155D-0027	2,513	$1,550	$1,650	$3,100	-	16
900-155D-0029	3,385	$1,550	$1,650	$3,100	-	32
900-155D-0047	2,500	$1,650	$1,750	$3,300	-	40
900-157D-0015	2,620	$1,029	$1,134	$2,058	-	42
900-157D-0023	2,873	$1,029	$1,134	$2,058	-	34
900-159D-0007	1,850	$1,100	$1,000	$2,000	-	26
900-161D-0013	3,264	$1,995	$2,145	$2,595	-	24
900-161D-0022	3,338	$1,795	$1,895	$2,595	-	36
900-161D-0024	3,665	$1,995	$2,195	$2,795	-	64
900-163D-0003	1,416	$1,250	-	$1,550	-	13
900-166D-0001	2,232	$1,089	$1,089	$1,789	-	43
900-167D-0001	2,017	$1,089	$1,089	$1,789	-	66
900-167D-0006	2,939	$1,189	$1,189	$1,989	-	38
900-167D-0007	3,016	$1,289	$1,289	$2,189	-	89

how can I find out if I can **afford** to build a home?

GET AN ACCURATE ESTIMATED COST-TO-BUILD REPORT

The most important question for someone wanting to build a new home is, "How much is it going to cost?" Obviously, you must have an accurate budget set prior to ordering house plans and beginning construction, or your dream home will quickly turn into a nightmare. Our goal is to make building your dream home a much simpler reality that's within reach thanks to the estimated cost-to-build report available for all of the home plans in this book and on our website, houseplansandmore.com.

Price is always the number one factor when selecting a new home. Price dictates the size and the quality of materials you will choose. So, it comes as no surprise that having an accurate building estimate prior to making your final decision on a home plan is quite possibly the most important step in the entire process.

If you feel you've found "the" home, before taking the step of purchasing plans, order an estimated cost-to-build report for the zip code where you want to build. When you order this report created specifically for you, it will educate you on all costs associated with building your new home. Simply order the cost-to-build report on houseplansandmore.com for the home you want to build and gain knowledge of the material and labor cost associated with the home. Not only does the report allow you to choose the quality of materials, you can select options in every aspect of the project from lot condition to contractor fees. This report will allow you to successfully manage your construction budget in all areas, clearly see where the majority of the costs lie, and save you money from start to finish.

Listed to the right are the categories included in the cost-to-build report. Each category breaks down labor cost, material cost, funds needed, and the report offers the ability to manipulate over/under adjustments if necessary.

BASIC INFORMATION includes your contact information, the state and zip code where you intend to build. First, select material class. It will include details of the home such as square footage, number of windows, fireplaces, balconies, and bathrooms. Deck, basement, or bonus room square footage is included. Garage location and number of bays, and your lot size are also included.

GENERAL SOFT COSTS include cost for plans, customizing (if applicable), building permits, pre-construction services, and planning expenses.

SITE WORK & UTILITIES include water, sewer, electric, and gas. Choose the type of site work you will need prior to building and if you'll need a driveway.

FOUNDATION is selected from a menu that lists the most common types.

FRAMING ROUGH SHELL calculates your rough framing costs including framing for fireplaces, balconies, decks, porches, basements and bonus rooms.

ROOFING includes several options so you can see how it will affect your overall price.

DRY OUT SHELL allows you to select doors, windows, siding and garage doors.

ELECTRICAL includes wiring and the quality of the light fixtures.

PLUMBING includes plumbing materials, plumbing fixtures, and fire proofing materials. It includes labor costs, and the ability to change fixture quality.

HVAC includes costs for both labor and materials.

INSULATION includes costs for both labor and materials.

FINISH SHELL includes drywall, interior doors and trim, stairs, shower doors, mirrors, and bath accessories - costs for both labor and materials.

CABINETS & VANITIES select the grade of your cabinets, vanities, kitchen countertops, and bathroom vanity materials, as well as appliances.

PAINTING includes all painting materials, their quality, and labor.

FLOORING includes over a dozen flooring material options.

SPECIAL EQUIPMENT NEEDS calculate cost for unforeseen expenses.

CONTRACTOR FEE / PROJECT MANAGER includes the cost of your cost-to-build report, project manager and/or general contractor fees. If you're doing the managing yourself, your costs will be tremendously lower in this portion.

LAND PAYOFF includes the cost of your land.

RESERVES / CLOSING COSTS includes interest, contingency reserves, and closing costs.

We've taken the guesswork out of what your new home will cost. Take control of your homebuilding project, determine the major expenses and save money. Easily supervise all costs, from labor to materials. Manage your home building with confidence and avoid costly mistakes and unforeseen expenses. If you want to order a Cost-To-Build Report for a home plan, visit houseplansandmore.com and search for the plan. Then, look for the orange button that says, "Request Your Report" and get started.

what kind of **plan package** do I need?

PLEASE NOTE: Not all plan packages listed below are available for every plan. Please refer to the home plan index on page 95 for plan options and pricing. For current pricing, all available plan packages and options, please visit houseplansandmore.com, or call 1-800-373-2646. The plan pricing shown in this book is subject to change without notice.

5-SET PLAN PACKAGE includes

five complete sets of construction drawings. Besides one set for yourself, additional sets of blueprints will be required for your lender, your local building department, your contractor, and any other tradespeople working on your project. Please note: These 5 sets of plans are copyrighted, so they can't be altered or copied.

8-SET PLAN PACKAGE includes

eight complete sets of construction drawings. Besides one set for yourself, additional sets of blueprints will be required for your lender, your local building department, your contractor, and any other tradespeople working on your project. Please note: These 8 sets of plans are copyrighted, so they can't be altered or copied.

REPRODUCIBLE MASTERS

is one complete paper set of construction drawings that can be modified. They include a one-time build copyright release that allows you to draw changes on the plans. This allows you, your builder, or local design professional to make the necessary drawing changes without the major expense of entirely redrawing the plans. Easily make minor drawing changes by using correction fluid to cover up small areas of the existing drawing, then draw in your modifications. Once the plan has been altered to fit your needs, you have the right to copy, or reproduce the modified plans as needed for building your home. Please note: The right of building only one home from these plans is licensed exclusively to the buyer. You may not use this design to build a second or multiple dwelling(s) without purchasing a multi-build license.

PDF FILE FORMAT is our most

popular plan option because of how fast you can receive them (usually within 24 to 48 hours Monday through Friday), and their ability to be easily shared via email with your contractor, subcontractors, and local building officials. The PDF file format is a complete set of construction drawings in an electronic file format. It includes a one-time build copyright release that allows you to make changes and copies of the plans. Typically you will receive a PDF file via email within 24-48 hours (Mon-Fri, 7:30am-4:30pm CST) allowing you to save money on shipping. Upon receiving, visit a local copy or print shop and print the number of plans you need to build your home, or print one and alter the plan by using correction fluid and drawing in your modifications. Please note: These are flat image files and cannot be altered electronically. PDF files are non-refundable and not returnable.

CAD FILE FORMAT is the actual

computer files for a plan directly from AutoCAD, or another computer aided design program. CAD files are the best option if you have a significant amount of changes to make to the plan, or if you need to make the plan fit your local codes. If you purchase a CAD File, it allows you, or a local design professional the ability to modify the plans electronically in a CAD program, so making changes to the plan is easier and less expensive than using a paper set of plans when modifying. A CAD package also includes a one-time build copyright release that allows you to legally make your changes, and print multiple copies of the plan. See the specific plan page for availability and pricing. Please note: CAD files are non-refundable and not returnable.

MIRROR REVERSE SETS

Sometimes a home fits a site better if it is flipped left to right. A mirror reverse set of plans is simply a mirror image of the original drawings causing the lettering and dimensions to read backwards. Therefore, when ordering a mirror reverse set of plans, you must purchase at least one set of the original plans to read from, and use the mirror reverse set for construction. Some plans offer right reading reverse for an additional fee. This means the plan has been redrawn by the designer as the mirrored version and can easily be read.

ADDITIONAL SETS You can order

additional sets of a plan for an additional fee. A 5-set, 8-set, or reproducible master must have been previously purchased. Please note: Only available within 90 days after purchase of a plan package.

2" X 6" EXTERIOR WALLS

2" x 6" exterior walls can be purchased for some plans for an additional fee (see houseplansandmore.com for availability and pricing).

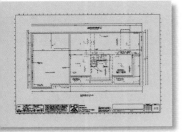

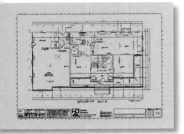

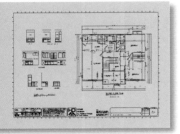

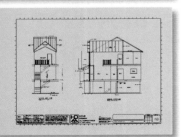

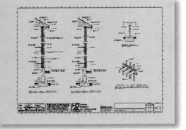

our **plan packages**
include...

Quality plans for building your future, with extras that provide unsurpassed value, ensure good construction and long-term enjoyment. A quality home - one that looks good, functions well, and provides years of enjoyment - is a product of many things - design, materials, and craftsmanship. But it's also the result of outstanding blueprints - the actual plans and specifications that tell the builder exactly how to build your home.

And with our BLUEPRINT PACKAGES you get the absolute best. A complete set of blueprints is available for every design in this book. These "working drawings" are highly detailed, resulting in two key benefits:

- **BETTER UNDERSTANDING BY THE CONTRACTOR OF HOW TO BUILD YOUR HOME AND...**

- **MORE ACCURATE CONSTRUCTION ESTIMATES THAT WILL SAVE YOU TIME AND MONEY.**

Below is a sample of the plan information included for most of the designs in this book. Specific details may vary with each designer's plan. While this information is typical of most plans, we cannot assure the inclusion of all the following referenced items. Please contact us at 1-800-373-2646 for a plan's specific information, including which of the following items are included.

1 cover sheet is included with many of the plans, the cover sheet is the artist's rendering of the exterior of the home. It will give you an idea of how your home will look when completed and landscaped.

2 foundation plan shows the layout of the basement, walk-out basement, crawl space, slab or pier foundation. All necessary notations and dimensions are included. See plan page for the foundation types included. If the home plan you choose does not have your desired foundation type, our Customer Service Representatives can advise you on how to customize your foundation to suit your specific needs or site conditions.

3 floor plans show the placement of walls, doors, closets, plumbing fixtures, electrical outlets, columns, and beams for each level of the home.

4 interior elevations provide views of special interior elements such as fireplaces, kitchen cabinets, built-in units and other features of the home.

5 exterior elevations illustrate the front, rear and both sides of the house, with all details of exterior materials and the required dimensions.

6 sections show detail views of the home or portions of the home as if it were sliced from the roof to the foundation. This sheet shows important areas such as load-bearing walls, stairs, joists, trusses and other structural elements, which are critical for proper construction.

7 details show how to construct certain components of your home, such as the roof system, stairs, deck, etc.

do you want to make **changes** to your plan?

We understand that sometimes it is difficult to find blueprints that meet all of your specific needs.
That is why we offer home plan modification services so you can build a home exactly the way you want it!

ARE YOU THINKING ABOUT CUSTOMIZING A PLAN?

If you're like many customers, you may want to make changes to your home plan to make it the dream home you've always wanted. That's where our expert design and modification partners come in. You won't find a more efficient and economic way to get your changes done than by using our home plan customizing services.

Whether it's enlarging a kitchen, adding a porch, or converting a crawl space to a basement, we can customize any plan and make it perfect for your needs. Simply create your wish list and let us go to work. Soon you'll have the blueprints for your new home and at a fraction of the cost of hiring a local architect!

IT'S EASY!

- We can customize any of plans in this book.
- We provide a FREE cost estimate for your home plan modifications within 24-48 hours (Monday through Friday).
- Average turn-around time to complete the modifications is typically 2-3 weeks.
- You will receive one-on-one design consultations.

CUSTOMIZING FACTS

- The average cost to have a house plan customized is typically less than 1 percent of the building costs — compare that to the national average of 7 percent of building costs.
- The average modification cost for a home is typically $800 to $1,500. This does not include the cost of purchasing the PDF file format of the blueprints, which is required to legally make plan changes.

OTHER HELPFUL INFORMATION

- Sketch, or make a specific list of changes you'd like to make on the Home Plan Modification Request Form.
- One of our home plan modification specialists will contact you within 24-48 hours with your free estimate.
- Upon accepting the estimate, you will need to purchase the PDF or CAD file format.
- A contract, which includes a specific list of changes and fees will be sent to you prior for your approval.
- Upon approving the contract, our design partners will keep you up to date by emailing sketches throughout the project.
- Plans can be converted to metric, or to a Barrier-free layout (also referred to as a universal home design, which allows easy mobility for an individual with limitations of any kind).

2 easy steps

1 visit houseplansandmore.com and click on the Resources tab at the top of the home page, or scan the QR code here to download the Home Plan Modification Request Form.

2 email your completed form to: customizehpm@designamerica.com, or fax it to: 651-602-5050. If you are not able to access the Internet, please call 1-800-373-2646 (Monday through Friday).

helpful **building** aids...

Your Blueprint Package will contain all of the necessary construction information you need to build your home. But, we also offer the following products and services to save you time and money in the building process.

MATERIAL LIST Many of the home plans in this book have a material list available for purchase that gives you the quantity, dimensions, and description of the building materials needed to construct the home (see the specific plan page for availability and pricing). Keep in mind, due to variations in local building code requirements, exact material quantities cannot be guaranteed. Note: Material lists are created with the standard foundation type only. Please review the material list and the construction drawings with your material supplier to verify measurements and quantities of the materials listed before ordering supplies.

THE LEGAL KIT Avoid many legal pitfalls and build your home with confidence using the forms and contracts featured in this kit. Included are request for proposal documents, various fixed price and cost plus contracts, instructions on how and when to use each form, warranty statements and more. Save time and money before you break ground on your new home or start a remodeling project. All forms are reproducible. This kit is ideal for homebuilders and contractors. Cost: $35.00

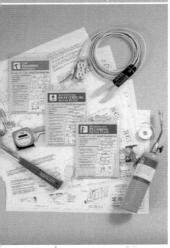

DETAIL PLAN PACKAGES- ELECTRICAL, FRAMING & PLUMBING
Three separate packages offer homebuilders details for constructing various foundations; numerous floor, wall and roof framing techniques; simple to complex residential wiring; sump and water softener hookups; plumbing connection methods; installation of septic systems, and more. Each package includes three dimensional illustrations and a glossary of terms. Purchase one or all three. Cost: $20.00 each or all three for $40.00 Please note: These drawings do not pertain to a specific home plan, but they include general guidelines and tips for construction in all 3 of these trades.

EXPRESS DELIVERY Most orders are processed within 24 hours of receipt. Please allow 7-10 business days for standard delivery. If you need to place a rush order, please call us by 11:00 am Monday through Friday CST and ask for express service (allow 1-2 business days). Please see page 101 for specific pricing information for shipping and handling.

TECHNICAL ASSISTANCE If you have questions about your blueprints, we offer technical assistance by calling 1-314-770-2228 (Monday through Friday). Whether it involves design modifications or field assistance, our home plans team is extremely familiar with all of our designs and will be happy to help you. We want your home to be everything you expect it to be.

before you **order**

PLEASE NOTE: Plan pricing is subject to change without notice. For current pricing, visit houseplansandmore.com, or call us at 1-800-373-2646.

BUILDING CODE REQUIREMENTS At the time the construction drawings were prepared, every effort was made to ensure that these plans and specifications met nationally recognized codes. These plans conform to most national building codes. Because building codes vary from area to area, some drawing modifications and/or the assistance of a professional designer or architect may be necessary to comply with your local codes, or to accommodate your specific building site conditions. We advise you to consult with your local building official, or a local builder for information regarding codes governing your area prior to ordering blueprints.

COPYRIGHT Plans are protected under Copyright Law. Reproduction by any means is strictly prohibited. The right of building only one structure from all plan packages is licensed exclusively to the buyer and the plans may not be resold unless by express written authorization from the home designer, or architect. You may not use this design to build a second or multiple structure(s) without purchasing a multi-build license. Each violation of the Copyright Law is punishable in a fine.

LICENSE TO BUILD When you purchase a "full set of construction drawings" from Design America, Inc., you are purchasing an exclusive one-time "License to Build," not the rights to the design. Design America, Inc. is granting you permission on behalf of the plan's designer or architect to use the construction drawings one-time for the building of the home. The construction drawings (also referred to as blueprints/plans and any derivative of that plan whether extensive or minor) are still owned and protected under copyright laws by the original designer. The blueprints/plans cannot be resold, transferred, rented, loaned or used by anyone other than the original purchaser of the "License to Build" without written consent from Design America, Inc. or the plan designer. If you are interested in building the plan more than once, please call 1-800-373-2646 and inquire about purchasing a Multi-Build License that will allow you to build a home design more than one time. Please note: A "full set of construction drawings" consists of either CAD files or PDF files.

shipping & handling charges

U.S. SHIPPING

(AK and HI express only)

Regular (allow 7-10 business days)	$30.00
Priority (allow 3-5 business days)	$50.00
Express* (allow 1-2 business days)	$70.00

CANADA SHIPPING**

Regular (allow 8-12 business days)	$50.00
Express* (allow 3-5 business days)	$100.00

OVERSEAS SHIPPING/INTERNATIONAL

Call, fax, or e-mail (customerservice@designamerica.com) for shipping costs.

* For express delivery please call us by 11:00 am Monday-Friday CST

** Orders may be subject to custom's fees and or duties/taxes.

Note: Shipping and handling does not apply on PDF Files and CAD Package orders. PDF and CAD orders will be emailed within 24-48 hours (Monday - Friday, 7:30am - 4:30pm CST) of purchase.

EXCHANGE POLICY Since blueprints are printed in response to your order, we cannot honor requests for refunds.

ORDER FORM

Please send me the following:

Plan Number: 900-_____

Select Foundation Type: **COST**
(Select ONE- see plan page for available options).
☐ Slab   ☐ Crawl space   ☐ Basement
☐ Walk-out basement   ☐ Pier
☐ Optional Foundation for an additional fee
    Enter foundation cost here $ _____
    (visit houseplansandmore.com for pricing)

PLAN PACKAGE

☐ CAD File $ _____
☐ PDF File Format (recommended) $ _____
☐ Reproducible Masters $ _____
☐ 8-Set Plan Package $ _____
☐ 5-Set Plan Package $ _____

See the Home Plan Index on page 95 for the most commonly ordered plan packages, or visit houseplansandmore.com to see current pricing and all plan package options available.

IMPORTANT EXTRAS

For pricing and availability of Material Lists, see the Home Plan Index on page 95. For the other plan options listed below, visit houseplansandmore.com, or call 1-800-373-2646.

☐ Additional plan sets*:
    _____ set(s) at $_____ per set $ _____
☐ Print in right-reading reverse:
    one-time additional fee of $_____ $ _____
☐ Print in mirror reverse:
    _____ set(s) at $_____ per set $ _____
    (where right reading reverse is not available)
☐ Material list (see page 95 for availability) $ _____
☐ Legal Kit (001D-9991, see page 100) $ _____
Detail Plan Packages: (see page 100)
    ☐ Framing   ☐ Electrical   ☐ Plumbing $ _____
    (001D-9992)   (001D-9993)   (001D-9994)
Shipping (see page 101) $ _____
SUBTOTAL $ _____
Sales Tax (MO residents only, add 8.238%) $ _____
TOTAL $ _____

*Available only within 90 days after purchase of plan.

HELPFUL TIPS
- You can upgrade to a different plan package within 90 days of your original plan purchase.
- Additional sets cannot be ordered without the purchase of a 5-Set, 8-Set, or Reproducible Masters.

Name _____
               (Please print or type)

Street _____
           (Please do not use a P.O. Box)

City_____State _____

Country _____ Zip _____

Daytime telephone   (_____) _____

E-Mail_____
        (For invoice and tracking information)

PAYMENT   ☐ Bank check/money order. No personal checks.

Make checks payable to Design America, Inc.

☐ MasterCard   ☐ VISA   ☐ DISCOVER   ☐ American Express Cards

Credit card number _____

Expiration date (mm/yy) _____ CID _____

Signature _____

☐ I hereby authorize Design America, Inc. to charge this purchase to my credit card.

Please check the appropriate box:

☐ Building home for myself

☐ Building home for someone else

ORDER ONLINE
houseplansandmore.com

ORDER TOLL-FREE BY PHONE
1-800-373-2646
Fax: 314-770-2226

EXPRESS DELIVERY
Most orders are processed within 24 hours of receipt. If you need to place a rush order, please call us by 11:00 am CST and ask for express service. Business Hours: Monday through Friday.

MAIL YOUR ORDER
Design America, Inc.
734 West Port Plaza, Suite #208
St. Louis, MO 63146

One-Story Home Plans   **SOURCE CODE 900**

Made in the USA
Monee, IL
14 November 2020